D1598019

DC/AC CIRCUITS:
PRINCIPLES AND PRACTICE

DC/AC CIRCUITS:
PRINCIPLES AND PRACTICE

LOUIS FRENZEL

&

PEOPLES COLLEGE

Delmar Publishers Inc.™

I(T)P™ An International Thomson Publishing Company

New York • Washington • Bonn • Boston • Detroit • Madrid • Melbourne • Mexico City • Paris
Singapore • Tokyo • Toronto • Washington • Albany NY • Belmont CA • Cincinnati OH

NOTICE TO THE READER

Cover Design: Spiral Design

Delmar Staff:

Publisher: Michael McDermott

Administrative Editor: Wendy J. Welch

Assistant Editor: Jenna Daniels

Senior Production Supervisor: Larry Main

Senior Project Editor: Christopher Chien

Art and Design Coordinator: Lisa Bower

COPYRIGHT © 1995

By Delmar Publishers Inc.

an International Thomson Publishing Company

I(T)P* The ITP logo is a trademark under license.

Printed in the United States of America

For more information, contact:

Delmar Publishers Inc.
3 Columbia Circle, Box 15015
Albany, New York 12212-5015

International Thomson Publishing
Berkshire House
168-173 High Holborn
London, WC1V7AA
England

Thomas Nelson Australia
102 Dodds Street
South Melbourne 3205
Victoria, Australia

Nelson Canada
1120 Birchmont Road
Scarborough, Ontario
M1K 5G4, Canada

International Thomson Publishing GmbH
Königswintererstr. 418
53227 Bonn
Germany

International Thomson Publishing Asia
221 Henderson Bldg. #05-10
Singapore 0315

International Thomson Publishing Japan
Kyowa Building, 3F
2-2-1 Hirakawa-cho
Chiyoda-ku, Tokyo 102
Japan

1 2 3 4 5 6 7 8 9 10 XXX 00 99 98 97 96 95

Library of Congress Cataloging-in-Publication Data
Frenzel, Louis E.
   DC/AC Circuits : principles and practice / Louis Frenzel & Peoples College
      p. cm.
   ISBN 0-8273-6338-9
   1. Electronic circuits—Experiments. 2. Electronic circuits—Alternating current—Experiments. 3. Electric circuits—Direct current—Experiments. I. Peoples College.
   II. Title.
   TK7867.F75   1994
   621.3815—dc20

94–7945

CIP

TABLE OF CONTENTS

PREFACE

Your electronic technician education would not be complete without some practical hands-on training using real electronic components, circuits, and equipment. On the job as a technician, you will build, test, measure, service, repair, adjust, install, maintain, operate, and otherwise work with electronic equipment. Your classroom work provides the theoretical background to understand this equipment. The lab work gives you the experience in applying the theory to the hardware.

This lab manual contains a series of experiments that provide demonstrations, test and measurement procedures, and other activities that allow you to verify and validate the theory you learn in class. The experiments also help you learn the important nitty-gritty details of component identification, circuit construction, circuit testing, and measurement techniques with test instruments that you will use throughout your career.

This manual is designed to be used with almost any modern technician level textbook teaching basic electronic theory and DC/AC circuit analysis. Each experiment gives you learning objectives and an introduction that reviews the fundamentals you will learn in the experiment. The procedure then leads you step-by-step through the process of building, demonstrating, analyzing, and testing of the primary electronic circuits that make up all electronic equipment. You will make calculations, take measurements, and draw conclusions about each circuit. Each experiment concludes with review questions to help you remember the key points.

I hope you enjoy the experiments in this manual. If you do, you will learn a great deal about the practical side of electronics, which will ultimately lead to your success on the job.

Good luck and best wishes.

Louis E. Frenzel

ACKNOWLEDGMENT

The experiments in this manual were originally developed for use in a distance education program offered by Peoples College in Kissimmee, Florida, which awards a Specialized Associate Degree in Electronics Technology. Because distance education is self-paced in nature, these lab experiments have been especially written for instructor-less instruction. Since an instructor is not always immediately available, special care has been taken to ensure that all necessary information has been provided. Detailed steps are given so that a successful outcome in each procedure is achieved. The experiments have not only been validated on hundreds of Peoples College students; most of the experiments have also been used successfully in my classes at Broward Community College in Coconut Creek, Florida.

I want to thank David L. Peoples, president of Peoples College and Southeastern Academy, for making this material available to others.

L. E. Frenzel
Parkland, Florida
December, 1993

PERFORMING THE EXPERIMENTS

To run the experiments in this manual, you will need the electronic components to construct the circuits, some method of interconnecting the components, and electronic test instruments to make your measurements. Each of these are described briefly.

Components

The resistors, capacitors, inductors, and other parts required by the experiments will be made available in your school lab. The parts and equipment you need are listed in the MATERIALS REQUIRED section of each experiment. The schematic diagrams of the experimental circuits also reinforce this list by showing specifically what parts are needed.

Breadboarding System

You will need some way to interconnect the components. This is usually done with a breadboarding system. This piece of equipment is also referred to as a trainer or prototyping unit. Its main feature is a breadboarding socket, which is a grid of metal connectors in a plastic housing that provides a fast, easy, and convenient way to connect electronic parts and wires without soldering. The wire leads of the components plug into the solderless connectors. Your instructor will explain the system used by your school.

Test Instruments

You will also need some test equipment to run the experiments. The main pieces of equipment needed are:

- Digital multimeter

- Oscilloscope

- Function generator

- Power supply

These are described next.

Digital Multimeter. The digital multimeter (DMM) is an instrument used to measure voltage, resistance, and current. It connects to a circuit with two test leads and displays the measured value on a 7-segment digital readout, either LCD or LED. An analog multimeter, also called a volt-ohmmeter (VOM), with its pointer-dial readout may also be used although its accuracy and precision are not as good as that of the DMM.

Oscilloscope. The oscilloscope uses a cathode ray tube (CRT) to display AC signals. A dual trace scope that permits two signals to be displayed simultaneously is preferred. The scope will allow you to measure voltage, period, frequency, and phase shift.

Function Generator. The function generator is also called a signal generator or a sine wave/audio oscillator. It generates a sine wave voltage of variable amplitude and frequency. It serves as the AC signal source for all of the AC experiments. The function generator also usually produces square waves and triangular waves.

Power Supply. The power supply produces a variable DC voltage for powering the experiments. Most lab power supplies permit the output to be continuously adjusted from zero up to about 15 to 30 volts DC. Many power supplies also contain built-in voltmeters. A dual power supply is preferred, as two independently adjustable DC supplies are needed in some experiments.

Section 1

DC
EXPERIMENTS

EXPERIMENT 1 ➤ Multimeter Familiarization

OBJECTIVES

When you complete this experiment, you will be able to measure voltage, current, and resistance using a digital multimeter.

MATERIALS REQUIRED

- Digital multimeter
- DC power supply
- one—9 volt battery
- one—Flashlight cell, size AA, C or D
- Resistors—½ watt:
  one–k ohm

INTRODUCTION

In performing your work as a technician, you will use a number of different types of test instruments to test, measure, and troubleshoot electronic equipment. The instrument that you will use the most is a multimeter. This is an instrument designed for measuring the three most important characteristics in any electronic circuit: voltage, current, and resistance. Most multimeters can measure DC and AC (sine wave) voltages, direct and alternating current, and DC resistance. Two test leads from the multimeter connect to a circuit or a component to perform these measurements. The multimeter is an extremely versatile instrument and it is one that you will use practically every day in your work. You will use the multimeter in all of the DC experiments in this lab manual. There are two basic types of multimeters in common use: analog and digital.

ANALOG MULTIMETERS

An analog multimeter uses a standard meter dial with a pointer. The value of voltage, current or resistance is read from the position of a pointer on the meter scale. Reading an analog multimeter is very much like determining the time from the hands on a clock. You must interpolate the number of seconds between the minutes markings. In the same way, on an analog multimeter you must determine or estimate the actual value by interpolating between the voltage, amperes or ohms markings on the meter scale.

Analog multimeters are inexpensive, reliable, and still widely used. Their main disadvantage is that they are less accurate and precise in measurement. In most cases, the accuracy of an analog multimeter is less than 2% of the full scale reading, which is quite adequate in most applications. However, there are many cases where more accurate measurements are desirable.

DIGITAL MULTIMETERS

A digital multimeter is like the analog multimeter in that it is a versatile instrument capable of voltage, current, and resistance measurements. The primary difference is that the measurement is displayed on a decimal readout. Most digital multimeters feature a liquid crystal display (LCD) similar to that used on digital watches. The value of current, voltage or resistance is displayed as decimal digits of the 7-segment format. Older digital multimeters use light-emitting diode (LED) displays. Some of the larger bench multimeters still use LED displays.

In addition to the convenience of an actual decimal display, digital multimeters also provide higher accuracy measurements. A good digital multimeter will provide an accuracy measurement of .5 to 1% within the actual value. Such accurate measurements are beneficial when testing electronic circuits because they provide the best information about circuit conditions. Digital multimeters also have better measurement resolution, which gives more precise measurements to a greater number of decimal places.

SUMMARY

A multimeter is an instrument that, when used properly, will tell you what's going on inside an electronic circuit. In this experiment, you will learn to use one. You will learn to measure DC voltage, direct current, and resistance.

PROCEDURE

1. Familiarize yourself with the multimeter. It could be either an analog or digital unit, depending upon which type is available in your lab. Examine the display and controls. Indicate the specific details of your meter in the spaces provided.

   a. Type of display _____
   b. Selection of measurement function (voltage, current, resistance)
      pushbutton switches _____
      slide switch _____
      rotary switch _____
   c. Selection of measurement range
      pushbutton switches _____
      slide switch _____
      rotary switch _____
   d. Selection of DC or AC measurements
      pushbutton switch _____
      slide switch _____
      rotary switch _____

2. Now, look at the test leads of the multimeter. The black lead is referred to as the common or ground lead. The red lead is referred to as the hot lead. The black lead is plugged into the COM jack on the front of the meter. The red lead plugs into the hole marked with ohm and volt symbols (Ω and V). The other jack(s) on the front of the meter is/are used when measuring current. The black lead always remains in the COM jack, but the red lead is switched to either the A or 10 A hole when making current measurements up to one ampere or ten amperes. For now, put the red lead in the Ω/V jack.

3. Before connecting the test leads, and particularly if the voltage or current to be measured is unknown, it is desirable to set the meter to the highest range possible. This will prevent meter damage. If the reading is too low, you can gradually switch to the lower ranges to obtain the best reading. When you know the range, and to obtain the most precise reading, always set the range to the position that is just above the value being measured. For example, if you want to measure 15 volts, set the switch to the 20-volt range rather than the 200-volt range.

   Most multimeters have the following ranges:

   - volts: 200 µV, 2 mV, 20 mV, 200 mV, 2 V, 20 V, 200 V, 1000 V
   - amps: 200 µA, 2 mA, 20 mA, 200 mA, 1A
   - ohms: 200 Ω, 2 kΩ, 20 kΩ, 200 kΩ, 2 MΩ

   If your meter has different ranges, record all of them in the format just given.

   Using the ranges given, indicate the optimum range for measuring each of the following electrical signals.

   a. 120 volts = _____ range
   b. 3 milliamperes = _____ range
   c. 470k ohms = _____ range

4. To learn how to use the multimeter, you will now measure DC voltages from batteries. A multimeter set up to measure voltage is called a voltmeter. Turn on the multimeter. Set the multimeter range and function switches to measure a 9-volt battery. Then touch the probes to the terminals of a 9-volt battery. Touch the red probe to the positive (+) terminal and the black probe to the negative (-) terminal. Read the voltage from the display and record it in the space provided.

   Battery voltage = _____ volts

5. Reverse the positions of the probes on the 9-volt battery terminals. Touch the black probe to the positive (+) terminal and the red probe to the negative (-) terminal and note the reading on the display. Write that value.

   Battery voltage (probes reversed) = _____ volts

   Explain the difference between the two readings.

6. Now measure the voltage from a standard flashlight cell. You can use the larger D cell, a smaller C size cell or the miniature AA cell. Before measuring the cell voltage, identify the positive and negative terminals of the cell. Then, measure the voltage by connecting the probes to the proper terminals. Use the 20-volt position on the meter switch. Reverse the probes and measure the voltage again. Record both readings in the spaces provided.

   Cell voltage = _____ volts
   Cell voltage (probes reversed) = _____ volts

   Again, explain any measurement differences.

7. Set the meter switch to the 2-volt position and again repeat the voltage measurement on the flashlight cell. Record your value of voltage.

   Cell voltage = _____ volts

   Explain the difference between the readings on the 2- and 20-volt ranges.

8. Next, measure the voltage from a lab power supply. Most supplies have an adjustable output voltage.

   Turn on the supply and connect the multimeter leads to its output. If the supply has its own built-in meter, adjust the output to 30 volts. If the supply cannot produce this high a voltage, set it to 14 volts. Use your multimeter to measure the output voltage if there is no built-in meter.

   Set the multimeter to the 200-volt range and measure the 30-volt output. If the output is 14 volts, use the 20-volt range on the multimeter to measure the output. Now, switch to the next lowest range (20 volts in the case of a 30-volt output and 2 volts with a 14-volt output). Describe what the multimeter display indicates.

9. Now you will use the multimeter to measure resistance. In this mode it is called an ohmmeter. Set the multimeter switch to the 2-kilohm position. Then touch the probes to the two leads of the 1-kilohm resistor (color code of brown-black-red-gold.) Record the measured value in the space provided.

   Resistance value = _____ ohms

10. Reverse the leads and again measure the resistor. What difference did you notice, if any?

11. Note the effect of an open or a short circuit. When set for ohmmeter operation, multimeters can be used for what is called a continuity measurement. In other words, they can detect an open circuit (infinite resistance) or a short circuit (zero ohm).

   With the meter set to the 2-kilohm range, touch the meter probes together. This represents a short. What resistance do you measure?

   Resistance of a short = _____ ohms

Now, leave the probes open, not touching one another or anything else. This is an open circuit. What does the meter display read? What resistance does this represent?

Meter reading = _____

Resistance of an open = _____ ohms

12. Next, you will measure current. The meter used this way makes it an ammeter. To do this, you will need to move the red probe to the jack marked A on the front of your multimeter. The black lead remains connected to the COM jack. Set the multimeter switch to the 20-mA current measuring position.

To measure current, you must actually construct a simple electrical circuit that will cause current to flow. You will do this using the 9-volt battery and 1-kilohm resistor. The circuit that you will connect is shown in schematic form in Figure 1–1. A current of one milliampere (1 mA) or .001 ampere will flow in this circuit.

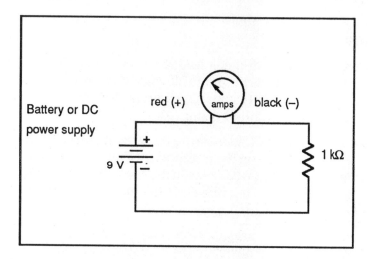

Figure 1–1 Multimeter Connected as Ammeter

To create the circuit, connect one lead of the resistor to the negative terminal of the 9-volt battery. Next, touch the red lead of the meter to the positive terminal of the battery and the black lead to the free end of the 1-kilohm resistor. Read the current on the display and record the value.

Circuit current = _____ mA

How does it compare to your calculated value? Explain any difference.

13. Reverse the meter probes and repeat step 12. How is the reading different? Explain.

REVIEW QUESTIONS

1. What multimeter range would you use to measure 2.7 volts?

   a. 200 mV
   b. 2 V
   c. 20 V
   d. 200 V

2. What is the main advantage of using the lowest possible range to measure a quantity?

   a. Avoids meter damage
   b. Better precision
   c. Faster measurement
   d. Greater accuracy

3. If the meter displays a 1 in the leftmost (most significant digit) position, it means that you:

   a. are measuring an open circuit or infinite resistance
   b. have the range set to a value too low for the quantity being measured
   c. Either a or b
   d. Neither a nor b

4. When measuring voltage and a negative sign appears on the display, it means that the red probe has what polarity with respect to the black probe (COM)?

   a. Negative
   b. Positive

5. Proper lead polarity must be observed when measuring resistance.

   a. True
   b. False

EXPERIMENT 2 ➤ Resistor Color Code

OBJECTIVES

When you complete this experiment, you will be able to read the resistor color code, calculate resistor tolerance, and measure resistance with an ohmmeter.

MATERIALS REQUIRED

- Digital multimeter
- Resistors supplied by the instructor

INTRODUCTION

Perhaps the most common electronic component is the resistor. Resistors offer a controlled amount of opposition to current flow in electronic circuits. The amount of resistance is expressed in ohms (Ω). *One ohm is defined as the amount of resistance through which one ampere of current will flow if one volt is applied to it.* In electronic circuits, resistor values range from a fraction to many millions of ohms. Large values of resistance are usually expressed in kilohms and megohms. A kilohm means one thousand ohms and is designated with the letter k (kΩ). A 10 k resistor has a value of 10 x 1000 = 10,000 ohms. One megohm means one million ohms and is designated by the letter M (MΩ). Therefore, a 2.2-M resistor has a value of 2,200,000 ohms.

Resistors come in standard values. The value of resistance is indicated by color bands on the resistor body. You must be able to glance at a resistor and immediately translate from the color code to the actual resistor value.

RESISTOR COLOR CODES

The resistor color code is easy to learn and use. Once you become familiar with it, you will be able to quickly and easily read resistor values. The purpose of this experiment is to introduce you to the color code and give you experience in reading these values.

The color code is given in Figure 2–1. The first two color bands on the resistor designate numerical values. The third color band indicates a multiplier. The multiplier indicates how many zeros must be added after the two numerical digits to give the final resistance value in ohms. The fourth color band is either silver or gold, is at the right, and designates the resistor tolerance. Most resistors used in electronics have either a 5% or 10% tolerance, meaning that the actual value of resistance is somewhere between ± 5% or ± 10% of the marked value.

Band Color	Value	Multiplier
Black	0	1
Brown	1	10
Red	2	100
Orange	3	1,000
Yellow	4	10,000
Green	5	100,000
Blue	6	1,000,000
Violet	7	10,000,000
Gray	8	100,000,000
White	9	1,000,000,000
Silver	10%	—
Gold	5%	—

Figure 2–1   Resistor Color Code

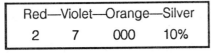

Red—Violet—Orange—Silver
2   7   000   10%

Figure 2–2   An Example of the Color Code

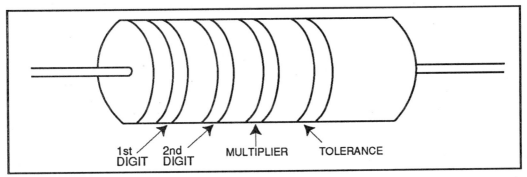

RESISTOR VALUES

Refer to Figure 2–2. To read a resistor value, first write down the numbers corresponding to the first two bands. In this case the numbers are 2 and 7. Next, write down the number of zeros indicated by the third band. In this case, orange means three, or in this case three zeros. You now have determined the actual resistor value, which is 27,000 ohms. Normally this would be written as 27 k ohms, the k replacing the three zeros.

Finally, the silver band indicates a tolerance of 10%. This means that the actual resistor value will be in a range between ±10% of the marked value. Ten percent of 27,000 ohms is:

$$27,000 \times .10 = 2,700 \text{ ohms}$$

The resistance range is:

$$27,000 - 2,700 = 24,300 \text{ ohms}$$
$$27,000 + 2,700 = 29,700 \text{ ohms}$$

The actual resistance value will be between 24,300 and 29,700 ohms. You can verify this by checking the value of the resistor with a multimeter.

Resistors also have a wattage rating, which indicates how much heat they can safely dissipate. Color-coded resistors come in standard wattage ratings of ⅛, ¼, ½, 1, and 2 watts (most resistors are of the ¼-watt size). The larger the resistor, the greater its power dissipation capability.

SUMMARY

In this experiment, and using Figure 2–3, you will take the resistors supplied by your instructor and determine their values and tolerances. You will also measure their values with your multimeter. This will provide you with sufficient initial experience to be able to read any resistor value supplied with this program.

Column 1	Column 2	Column 3	Column 4	Column 5
Color Code	Resistance	Tolerance	Range	Measured Value
red-violet-orange-silver	27,000	10%	27,300–28,445	28,445

Figure 2–3 Table for Recording Resistor Values

PROCEDURE

1. Write the resistor color code of each of the resistors supplied by your instructor in the left hand-column of Figure 2–3. It does not matter in which order you *list* the resistors. Be sure, however, as you write down the color code of each resistor, that you are reading it correctly from left to right. One way to be sure that you have correctly positioned the resistor is to ensure that the gold or silver tolerance band is always on the right. Record all of the resistor color codes in the table of Figure 2–3 before you go on to the next step. The first row in Figure 2–3 shows the format using the example given in the Introduction to this chapter.

2. Translate the color code into the correct value. Record the resistance value in the second column of Figure 2–3. Record all the resistor values before going ahead to the next step. The tolerance should be written in the third column.

3. Using the tolerance value you recorded in column 3, compute the resistance range for each resistor. That is, determine the upper and lower values of the resistance range designated by the tolerance. Record your figures in column 4 of Figure 2–3.

4. Next, using your digital multimeter, measure the value of each resistor. Use the resistance range that will provide the greatest precision and resolution. As you measure each resistor value, record its value in column 5 of Figure 2–3.

5. Now, compare the actual measured value to the marked value and the tolerance range. Verify that the measured value is within the tolerance range. If any of the measured values are outside of the tolerance range, place a check mark beside those resistors.

REVIEW QUESTIONS

1. The shorthand way to express a resistance value of 15,000,000 ohms is:

   a. 15 k
   b. 1.5 M
   c. 1500 k
   d. 15 M

2. A resistor with a color code of blue-gray-yellow-silver has a value of:

   a. 86 k, 5%
   b. 680 k, 10%
   c. 860 k, 5%
   d. 6.8 M, 10%

3. What is the resistance range of a 2.2 k ohm, 5% resistor?

   a. 2090–2310 ohms
   b. 1980–2420 ohms
   c. 2090–2200 ohms
   d. 2200–2310 ohms

4. A multiplier of 10,000,000 is represented by what color?

    a. Green
    b. Blue
    c. Violet
    d. Gray

5. The size of a resistor usually indicates its:

    a. ohmic value
    b. tolerance
    c. resistance range
    d. wattage rating

EXPERIMENT 3 ➤ Ohm's Law

OBJECTIVE

When you complete this experiment, you will be able to calculate and measure current, voltage, and resistance in an electrical circuit to verify Ohm's law.

MATERIALS REQUIRED

- Digital multimeter
- Breadboarding socket
- DC power supply
- Resistors—¼ watt, 5%:
  one–470 ohms
  one–680 ohms
  one–2.2 kΩ
  one–4.7 kΩ

INTRODUCTION

Perhaps the most important basic electrical concept is Ohm's law. This is the relationship that exists between the current, voltage, and resistance in an electrical or electronic circuit. A voltage source is connected to a resistance and causes current to flow. The amount of current is determined by the amount of voltage applied and the value of the resistance. Ohm's law states that *the current is directly proportional to the voltage and inversely proportional to the resistance.* This relationship is expressed in the simple electrical formula:

$$I = V/R$$

In this expression, I is the current in amperes, V is the voltage in volts, and R is the resistance in ohms. Values of current can be quickly computed using a calculator. For example, how much current flows in a 2.2 k ohm resistor connected to a 6-volt source? The answer is:

$$I = 6/2.2 \text{ k} = 6/2,200 = .00273 \text{ amperes}$$

This value can also be expressed in milliamperes, or 2.73 mA.

As you have learned, the basic Ohm's law formula can be rearranged using algebra so that you can calculate either the voltage or the resistance. These other formulas are:

$$V = IR$$

$$R = V/I$$

DC Experiments

13

In your electronics work you will use Ohm's law regularly. Even in the most complex circuits you will apply this relationship. It is important that you can make these calculations regardless of the conditions.

CALCULATING THE LAW

To make the Ohm's law calculation, you *must know* two of the three values. The values of current, voltage, and resistance can be obtained in a variety of ways. Resistor values can be determined from the color code of a resistor or by actually measuring the resistor value. Current is usually determined by measurement. The voltage value is often easy to determine because it comes from a source whose output voltage is fixed and known. For example, if a flashlight cell is used, then you know that the voltage value is 1.5 volts. All batteries have standard output voltage values, as do many power supplies. If the voltage is not known, however, it can be measured.

SUMMARY

In this experiment you will build several simple electrical circuits and make electrical measurements so you can perform Ohm's law calculations. Given a circuit, you will be able to calculate the necessary values. Then you will construct the various circuits and verify those values through measurement.

PROCEDURE

1. Refer to the circuit in Figure 3–1. Given the values of voltage and resistance, calculate the amount of current that will flow. Record your value in the space provided.

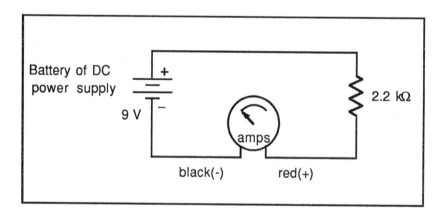

Figure 3–1

$I =$ _____ mA (calculated)

2. Wire the circuit shown in Figure 3–1. Use a DC power supply set to give 9 volts.

You will use the multimeter to measure the current in this circuit. Set the multimeter range to an appropriate value based on your calculation in Step 1. Be sure to plug the red lead into the A jack on the meter.

3. Once the circuit has been constructed, touch the black probe to the negative terminal of the battery or power supply and the red probe to the unconnected resistor lead. Read the current from the meter. Record the value.

$$I = \underline{\hspace{5cm}} \text{ mA (measured)}$$

4. Compare your calculated and measured values. Explain the reasons for any differences.

5. Double the supply voltage given in Figure 3–1. What is the new circuit supply voltage?

$$\text{Supply voltage} = \underline{\hspace{5cm}} \text{ volts}$$

6. Using the new supply voltage and the resistor value used previously, calculate the new current.

$$I = \underline{\hspace{5cm}} \text{ mA (calculated)}$$

7. Measure the new current by connecting the multimeter probes to the circuit as described earlier.

$$I = \underline{\hspace{5cm}} \text{ mA (measured)}$$

8. Compare the currents in steps 1 and 6 and in steps 3 and 7. How did the current change when the supply voltage changed? Does the change comply with Ohm's law? Explain.

9. Disconnect the circuit shown in Figure 3–1 and wire the circuit shown in Figure 3–2.

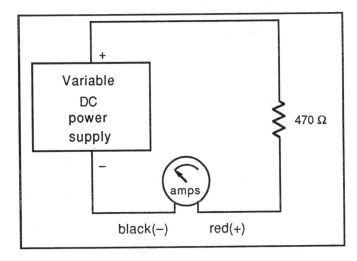

Figure 3–2

10. Measure the amount of current flowing in the circuit using the procedure described earlier. Record your value.

$$I = \underline{\hspace{5cm}} \text{ mA (measured)}$$

11. Using the value of current you measured, calculate the resistor value using Ohm's law. Record the resistor value.

$$R = \underline{\hspace{5cm}} \text{ ohms (calculated)}$$

12. Now, read the resistor color code and record its value.

$$R = \underline{\hspace{5cm}} \text{ ohms (color code)}$$

13. Compare the value of resistance calculated using the measured current to the value of the resistor as determined by the color code. Explain any difference.

14. Change the value of the resistor in Figure 3–2 to 2.2 k ohms.

15. Calculate the expected current.

$$I = \underline{\hspace{5cm}} \text{ mA (calculated)}$$

16. Measure the current using the procedure you used in the previous steps.

$$I = \underline{\hspace{5cm}} \text{ mA (measured)}$$

17. Compare the current you measured in step 16 to that you measured in step 10. How does the current change as the resistance changes? Are your results consistent with Ohm's law? Explain.

18. Use a variable DC power supply with the circuit in Figure 3–2 and a 2.2 k ohm resistor. Vary the voltage from 0 to 12 volts in 2-volt steps. Measure the current at each voltage point.

19. Repeat step 18 using a 470-ohm resistor. Using the data in steps 18 and 19, plot current vs. voltage graphs on linear graph paper.

REVIEW QUESTIONS

1. An unknown voltage source is connected to a 39 k resistor. You measured a current of .31 mA. The applied voltage must be about:

   a. 12 volts
   b. 28 volts
   c. 57 volts
   d. 126 volts

2. Decreasing the voltage across a resistor causes the current to:

   a. increase
   b. decrease
   c. remain the same
   d. drop to zero

3. Decreasing the resistance connected to a voltage source causes the current to:

   a. increase
   b. decrease
   c. remain the same
   b. drop to zero

4. Refer to your graph for step 19. The rate of change of current with respect to the change in voltage is:

   a. greater with a smaller resistor
   b. greater with a larger resistor
   c. less with a smaller resistor
   d. the same with any value resistor

5. To measure current with a multimeter, how must it be connected into the circuit?

   a. Backwards
   b. Parallel
   c. Series
   d. With leads reversed

EXPERIMENT 4 ➤ Series Circuits

OBJECTIVES

When you complete this experiment, you will be able to calculate the total resistance of several resistors in series and use Kirchhoff's voltage law to make series circuit calculations and measurements.

MATERIALS REQUIRED

- Digital multimeter
- Breadboarding socket
- DC power supply
- Resistors—¼ watt, 5%:
  one–470 ohms
  one–680 ohms
  one–2.2 kΩ
  one–4.7 kΩ
  one–Light emitting diode (LED)

INTRODUCTION

There are two *basic* ways to connect electronic components to a voltage source. In a series circuit, all of the components are connected end-to-end to form a single chain that is connected to the voltage source. In a parallel circuit (Experiment 5), all of the individual components are *each* connected directly across the voltage source. Of course, there are more complex circuits using some combination of series and parallel connections (Experiment 6). In this experiment, you will learn how to connect series circuits and make various calculations and measurements.

First, learn how to compute the total resistance of a series circuit. *When two or more resistors are connected in series, the total resistance of the combination is simply the sum of the individual resistances.*

A typical series circuit is shown in Figure 4–1. The total resistance, R_T, is the sum of the individual resistors or:

$$R_T = R_1 + R_2 + R_3$$

With the resistor values shown, the total resistance is:

$$R_T = 50 + 75 + 30 = 155 \text{ ohms}$$

The three resistors could be replaced by a single 155-ohm resistor with no change in circuit current.

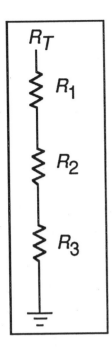

Figure 4–1

VOLTAGE DROPS

When current flows through a series circuit, the voltage drops appear across each resistance. Figure 4–1 shows a series circuit with the voltages across each resistance indicated. Note the polarity of the voltage drop across each resistor. The voltage across each resistor, of course, can be determined by Ohm's law. In this case, the total circuit current is multiplied by each resistor value to get the corresponding voltage drop. For example, the voltage across R_2 is:

$$V_2 = I_{R_2}$$

An extremely important characteristic of a series circuit to remember is that the *sum* of the individual voltage drops equals the source voltage. Note in Figure 4–1 that if the voltages across R_1, R_2, and R_3 are added together, the total is also the same as the applied voltage.

$$V_S = V_1 + V_2 + V_3$$

This basic relationship is known as Kirchhoff's voltage law. It is extremely useful in making series circuit calculations. By using this relationship in various ways, series circuits are easily analyzed and designed.

CURRENT LIMITING RESISTORS

An example of the use of Kirchhoff's law is the calculation of *series dropping* resistors. A series dropping resistor is simply a resistor connected in series with some device to lower the voltage applied to the device. Such a resistor is also referred to as a current limiting resistor. It is often necessary to operate, for example, a light bulb from a higher voltage source. In order to prevent the device from being damaged by over-voltage, a resistor is connected in series with the device to drop the excessive amount of voltage, Figure 4–2. Also, it might be necessary to operate a 3-volt bulb from a 12-volt battery. If the full 12 volts is applied to the bulb, however, the bulb will burn out. But, by connecting the correct value of resistor in series with the bulb, the excess 9 volts will appear across the resistor, leaving only the proper amount across the bulb. In short, the resistor is chosen to limit the current to the maximum safe value for the bulb.

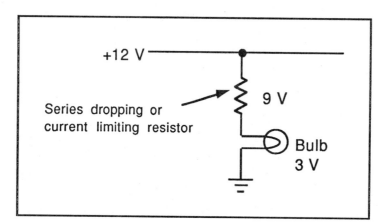

Figure 4–2

SUMMARY

In this experiment, you will verify that the total resistance of a series circuit is the sum of the individual resistors. Then you will verify Kirchhoff's voltage law. Finally, you will calculate a series dropping resistor for a light-emitting diode.

PROCEDURE

1. Using the values given in Figure 4–3, calculate the total circuit resistance.

$$R_T = \text{_____} \text{ ohms (calculated)}$$

2. Wire the circuit shown in Figure 4–3.

3. Using your multimeter, measure the total circuit resistance.

$$R_T = \text{_____} \text{ ohms (measured)}$$

4. Compare your calculated and measured values and account for any differences.

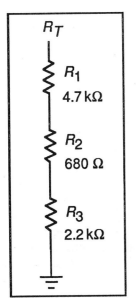

Figure 4–3

5. Connect a 9-volt power supply to the circuit. See Figure 4–4.

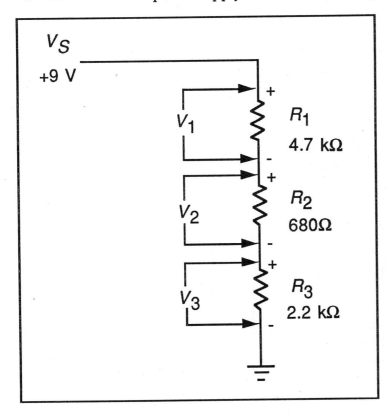

Figure 4–4

6. Using the value of total resistance you computed earlier, calculate and enter the expected circuit current with 9 volts applied.

$$I = \underline{\hspace{4cm}} \text{ mA}$$

7. Now, using Ohm's law, calculate and record the voltage across each resistor.

$$V_1 = \underline{\hspace{3cm}} \text{ volts}$$
$$V_2 = \underline{\hspace{3cm}} \text{ volts}$$
$$V_3 = \underline{\hspace{3cm}} \text{ volts}$$

8. Now calculate and record the sum of the individual voltage drops.

$$V_S = V_1 + V_2 + V_3 = \underline{\hspace{4cm}} \text{ volts}$$

9. Using your multimeter, measure the voltage drop across each resistor. Remember that you will be measuring DC voltages and you will need to touch the multimeter probes across the resistors in the correct direction to obtain the right polarity readings. Note the polarities of the voltage drops in the circuit of Figure 4–4. Record your measured voltage drops and then compute their sum.

$$V_1 = \underline{\hspace{3cm}} \text{ volts}$$
$$V_2 = \underline{\hspace{3cm}} \text{ volts}$$
$$V_3 = \underline{\hspace{3cm}} \text{ volts}$$
$$V_S = \underline{\hspace{3cm}} \text{ volts}$$

10. Compare your measured and computed values for the voltage drops and the total voltage. Do the voltage drops add up to equal the source voltage?

11. Refer to Figure 4–5. Here a light-emitting diode is to be operated from a 9-volt power supply. Your job is to determine the value of the series dropping resistor R_1. The light emitting diode has a voltage drop across it of about 2 volts when it is conducting. A current of 15 mA is required for moderate brilliance. Calculate the value of the series dropping resistance required. Record the value.

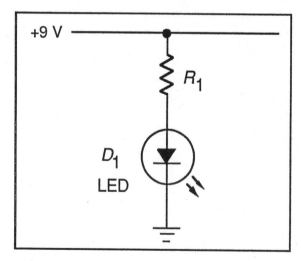

Figure 4–5

$$R_1 = \underline{\hspace{3cm}} \text{ ohms}$$

12. Select the closest available resistor value from those on hand in your lab. Then construct the circuit shown in Figure 4–5. Be sure to observe the polarity of both the battery connections and the LED leads. The negative lead of the power supply should connect to the cathode lead of the LED, which is identified by the flat side on the housing. In the LED symbol, the arrow head is the anode while the straight line is the cathode.

13. If you calculated and selected the correct resistor value, the LED should light. Measure the voltage drops across the LED and R_1.

V_1 = _____volts
V_{LED} = _____volts
V_S = _____volts

14. Does the sum of the circuit voltage drops equal the source voltage? How do your measured and calculated values compare? Explain any differences.

REVIEW QUESTIONS

1. Two resistors (R_1 and R_2) are connected in series. R_1 = 68 ohms. The total resistance (R_T) is 150 ohms. What is the value of R_2?

   a. 28 ohms
   b. 82 ohms
   c. 86 ohms
   d. 218 ohms

2. In a series circuit, the resistor voltage drops are V_1 = 2.5 V, V_2 = 1.8 V, V_3 = 3.4 V, and V_4 = 6.9 V. What is the source voltage?

   a. 10.3 volts
   b. 12.1 volts
   c. 12.8 volts
   d. 14.6 volts

3. The current through all resistors in a series circuit is the same.

   a. True
   b. False

4. A 6-volt bulb draws a current of .15 A. To operate it from a 15-volt supply, you need a series dropping resistor of:

   a. 33 ohms
   b. 50 ohms
   c. 60 ohms
   d. 120 ohms

5. A series circuit has resistors of 180 Ω, 2.7 kΩ, 5.6 kΩ, and 6.8 kΩ. The smallest voltage drop appears across which resistor?

   a. 180 ohms
   b. 2.7 k ohms
   c. 5.6 k ohms
   d. 6.8 k ohms

EXPERIMENT 5 ➤ Parallel Circuits

OBJECTIVES

When you complete this experiment, you will be able to calculate the total value of resistors in parallel and verify Kirchhoff's current law for parallel circuits.

MATERIALS REQUIRED

- Digital multimeter
- Breadboarding socket
- DC power supply
- Resistors—¼ watt, 5%:
  one–2.2 kΩ
  one–4.7 kΩ
  one–10 kΩ

INTRODUCTION

In a parallel circuit all of the resistors or other circuit components are connected directly across the voltage source. Figure 5–1 illustrates a parallel circuit where four resistors are connected directly to the voltage source. The voltage source causes current to flow in each resistor. Each resistor or other circuit element is referred to as one branch of the parallel circuit.

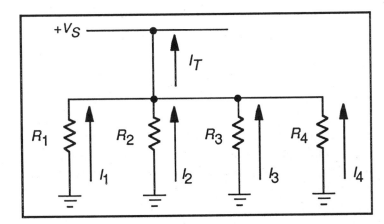

Figure 5–1

The total current drawn from the voltage source in Figure 5–1 is simply the sum of the currents flowing in each branch of the parallel circuit. In this case, the total circuit current is:

$$I_T = I_1 + I_2 + I_3 + I_4$$

This relationship is known as Kirchhoff's current law for parallel circuits. Stated again, it says that *the sum of the individual branch currents in a parallel circuit is equal to the total current drawn from the voltage source.* Kirchhoff's current law makes the analysis and design of parallel circuits easy.

The total and branch currents in a parallel circuit can either be calculated or measured. However, there are some applications where one of the branch currents may not be known. In such a case, through a combination of calculations and measurements, the unknown branch current can be determined. For example, assume that the current through R_2 in Figure 5–1 is not known. You can easily determine it by algebraically rearranging the basic formula to solve for I_2. You simply subtract the known branch currents from the total current to obtain the unknown value.

$$I_2 = I_T - I_1 - I_3 - I_4$$

or

$$I_2 = I_T - (I_1 + I_3 + I_4)$$

By measuring and/or calculating the values, the unknown current can be determined.

To calculate the total resistance represented by two or more resistors in parallel, special formulas are used. When two resistors are connected in parallel, the total resistance of the combination is determined with the simple expression:

$$R_T = R_1(R_2)/(R_1 + R_2)$$

When three or more resistors are connected in parallel, this formula is used:

$$R_T = 1/(1/R_1 + 1/R_2 + 1/R_3 + ...)$$

While this formula looks complex, it is relatively simple to use if you have an electronic calculator. Simply plug in the values and compute the reciprocals. The reciprocal of a number is one divided by that number $(1/x)$. The reciprocal of R_1 is $1/R_1$. The reciprocals are then added and the total reciprocal of the combination is found to compute the total resistance value.

SUMMARY

In this experiment, you are going to verify the use of these parallel resistance formulas. Then, you will make calculations and measurements on a typical parallel circuit to verify Kirchhoff's current law.

PROCEDURE

1. Construct the circuit shown in Figure 5–2.

2. Using the values given in Figure 5–2, calculate the total circuit resistance.

$R_T =$ _____ohms

3. Now use your multimeter to measure the total resistance of the parallel combination in Figure 5–2.

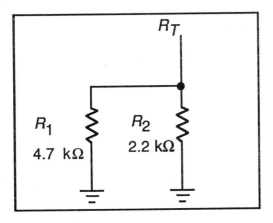

Figure 5–2

$$R_T = \underline{\hspace{4cm}}\text{ohms}$$

4. Compare your computed and measured values in steps 2 and 3 and account for any differences.

5. Wire the parallel circuit shown in Figure 5–3 by adding a 10 k ohm resistor in parallel with the other two.

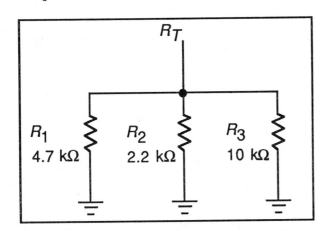

Figure 5–3

6. Using the reciprocal formula given earlier, calculate the total resistance of the parallel combination in Figure 5–3.

$$R_T = \underline{\hspace{4cm}}\text{ ohms}$$

7. Using your multimeter, measure the resistance of the circuit in Figure 5–3.

$$R_T = \underline{\hspace{4cm}}\text{ ohms}$$

8. Compare your calculated and measured values and account for any differences.

9. Connect a 9-volt power supply across the parallel circuit as shown in Figure 5–4.

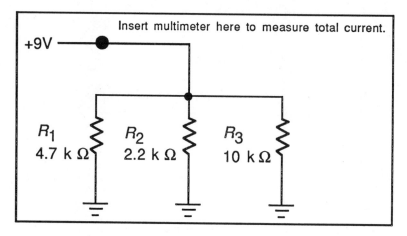

Figure 5–4

10. Using the total resistance you calculated in step 6, calculate the expected total circuit current.

$$I_T = \text{\underline{\hspace{4cm}}} \text{ mA}$$

11. Set your multimeter to measure current in the milliampere range. Connect the red lead to the A jack. Connect the ammeter between the positive lead of the power supply and your parallel circuit. Be sure to observe the correct polarity connections. Then, measure the total circuit current and record the value.

$$I_T = \text{\underline{\hspace{4cm}}} \text{ mA}$$

12. Disconnect the multimeter and reconnect the positive terminal of the power supply. Then connect the multimeter in series with each of the parallel branch resistors, one at a time, and measure the current through each. One way to physically do this is illustrated in Figure 5–5. Simply disconnect one lead of the resistor whose current you wish to measure and connect the multimeter between that resistor lead and the common lead to the negative terminal of the power supply. When you complete the current measurement for each resistor, return its connection to the negative terminal of the power supply before disconnecting another. Use this procedure to measure each resistor current and record the values.

$$I_1 = \text{\underline{\hspace{4cm}}} \text{ mA}$$
$$I_2 = \text{\underline{\hspace{4cm}}} \text{ mA}$$
$$I_3 = \text{\underline{\hspace{4cm}}} \text{ mA}$$

13. Now using your measured values, compute the total circuit current.

$$I_T = \text{\underline{\hspace{4cm}}} \text{ mA}$$

14. Compare the measured values of the resistor currents with the values you computed earlier. Also, compare the computed and measured values of total current. Account for any differences.

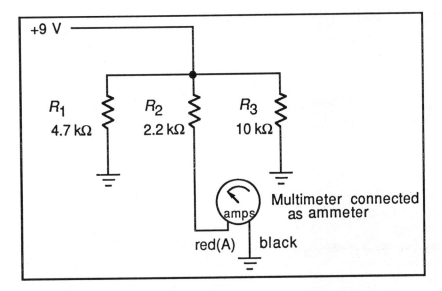

+9 V

R_1
4.7 kΩ

R_2
2.2 kΩ

R_3
10 kΩ

Multimeter connected
as ammeter

amps

red(A)   black

Figure 5–5

REVIEW QUESTIONS

1. Five 10k resistors are connected in parallel. The total resistance is:

   a. 2 k ohms
   b. 10 k ohms
   c. 25 ohms
   d. 50 k ohms

2. In a parallel circuit, the highest branch current appears in the:

   a. largest resistor
   b. smallest resistor

3. In a parallel circuit, the total resistance is less than the smallest branch resistance.

   a. True
   b. False

4. A parallel circuit has two branches. One has a current $I_1 = 40$ mA. The total current $I_T = 128$ mA. The other branch current I_2 is:

   a. 51 mA
   b. 68 mA
   c. 88 mA
   d. 168 mA

5. If one resistor in a parallel circuit of four resistors is removed, the total circuit resistance will:

   a. drop to zero
   b. remain the same
   c. decrease
   d. increase

DC Experiments

EXPERIMENT 6 ➤ Combination Series/Parallel Circuits

OBJECTIVE

When you complete this experiment, you will be able to calculate the total resistance value of a complex series/parallel resistance network and determine the voltage across or current through any component in the circuit.

MATERIALS REQUIRED

- Digital multimeter
- Breadboarding socket
- DC power supply
- one—Battery clip with leads
- Resistors, ¼ watt, 5%:
  one—470Ω
  one—680Ω
  one—2.2 kΩ
  one—4.7 kΩ
  two—10 kΩ

INTRODUCTION

Most practical electronic circuits often appear to be some complex combination of series and parallel circuits. You must know how to calculate not only the total circuit resistance, and also the value of current *through* or voltage *across* any of the individual components. Making calculations in such circuits are no more difficult than working with simple series or parallel circuits. The reason is simple: any complex circuit can be quickly and easily divided into many smaller, simpler circuits. By using the techniques you learned earlier for series and parallel circuits, you will have no difficulty in analyzing the larger and more complex ones.

To reword: To make calculations in such a circuit, *simply view the circuit as many small, simple circuits.* Start by calculating the circuits farthest from the voltage source. Then work your way toward the voltage source, combining your individual results. Gradually, you will compute a final total of equivalent circuit resistance.

Once that total circuit resistance is known, calculate the total circuit current drawn from a voltage source. Using this current, voltage drops can be calculated using Kirchhoff's laws. Through the continuous application of Ohm's and Kirchhoff's laws, you can determine the voltage or current at any point in the circuit.

SUMMARY

In this experiment, you will construct a complex series/parallel resistive network. You will calculate its total resistance and verify it by measurement. Then you will compute current and voltage values at specific points in the circuit. Again, you will verify your calculations with actual measurements.

PROCEDURE

1. Construct the circuit shown in Figure 6–1, but do not connect the power supply until told to do so. This is one of the more complex circuits you have had to wire so far, so take your time and be careful. At this point it is still a good idea to make the actual physical arrangement of resistors on the breadboarding socket as close to the schematic diagram positioning as possible. This will help you keep track of each of the resistors and will make the various current and voltage measurements much easier. Once you have completed the wiring, go back and double check it for errors.

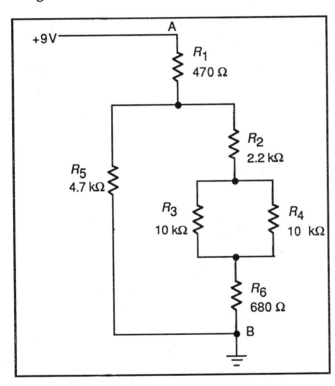

Figure 6–1

2. Using the procedures you learned in earlier experiments, calculate the total circuit resistance between points A and B. Later you will connect the battery to these points.

$R_T = $ _____ ohms (calculated)

3. Using your multimeter, measure the total resistance between points A and B on your circuit.

$$R_T = \underline{\hspace{5cm}} \text{ ohms (measured)}$$

4. Connect a 9-volt power supply to the circuit at terminals A and B.

5. Calculate the current through resistor R_5.

$$I_{R_5} = \underline{\hspace{5cm}} \text{mA (calculated)}$$

6. Calculate the voltage drop across resistors R_3 and R_4.

$$V_{R_{3-4}} = \underline{\hspace{5cm}} \text{volts (calculated)}$$

7. Using your multimeter, measure the current through resistor R_5.

$$I_{R_5} = = \underline{\hspace{5cm}} \text{mA (measured)}$$

8. Measure the voltage across resistors R_3 and R_4.

$$V_{R_{3-4}} = \underline{\hspace{5cm}} \text{volts (measured)}$$

9. How do your computed and measured values compare? Explain any differences.

REVIEW QUESTIONS

1. In Figure 6–1, what is the current through R_3?

   a. .15 mA
   b. .32 mA
   c. .44mA
   d. .89mA

2. In calculating the total resistance of a series-parallel combination circuit, begin as far away from the voltage source as possible.

   a. True
   b. False

3. The main cause of the difference between calculated and measured values is:

   a. voltage variation
   b. meter error
   c. computational errors
   d. resistor tolerance

4. With the power supply connected to A and B as shown in Figure 6–1, in which direction do electrons flow through R_5?

    a. left to right
    b. right to left

5. What is the polarity of the voltage across R_2?

    a. top +, bottom –
    b. top –, bottom +

EXPERIMENT 7 ➤ Voltage Dividers

OBJECTIVES

When you complete this experiment, you will be able to calculate the output voltage of a voltage divider with and without a load, and demonstrate that a potentiometer is a variable voltage divider.

MATERIALS REQUIRED

- Digital multimeter
- Breadboarding socket
- DC power supply
- one—10 kΩ potentiometer
- Resistors—¼ watt, 5%:
  one–220 Ω
  one–470 Ω
  one–1 k Ω
  one–2.2 kΩ
  one–3.3 kΩ
  one–10 kΩ
  one–100 kΩ

INTRODUCTION

A *voltage divider is a resistive network whose output voltage is less than the input voltage.* In electronic circuits it is frequently necessary to reduce the voltage level of a signal. This is most easily done with a two-resistor circuit known as a voltage divider. The input voltage is applied across the two resistors and the output voltage is taken from across one of them. The values of the resistors are selected so that the output voltage is some desired fraction of the input voltage.

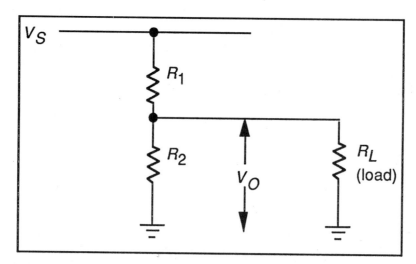

Figure 7–1

A common voltage divider is shown in Figure 7–1. You can use Ohm's law to calculate the output voltage if the input voltage and resistor values are known. However, the following formula speeds up and simplifies this process.

$$V_O = V_S R_2 / (R_1 + R_2)$$

The output voltage computed with this formula assumes that there is *no load* on the circuit. Should a finite value of load resistance appear across R_2, the output voltage will be lower than that computed. If the load resistance approaches the value of R_2, then it will draw more and more current from the circuit. This will redistribute the voltage drops in the circuit and the output voltage can no longer be that computed with the formula.

To determine the output of a voltage divider *with* a load, you can use standard Ohm's and Kirchhoff's laws calculating techniques as you did in the previous experiment to predict the output voltage. In many applications, however, this is not necessary. If the load resistance is made high with respect to the value of R_2, the output voltage will be very nearly equal to that produced by the formula. As a rule of thumb, the load resistance should be ten or more times the value of R_2. The higher the value of the load resistance with respect to R_2, the closer the output voltage comes to the value computed with the formula.

THE POTENTIOMETER

One of the most useful electronic components is the potentiometer, which is in effect, a variable voltage divider. *A potentiometer is a variable resistor with three terminals*, Figure 7–2. The center terminal connects to a moveable arm that can be positioned at any point on the resistance element, allowing a portion of the total applied voltage to be tapped off. The arm can be varied from one end of the resistance element to the other, thereby permitting any voltage value between the input source voltage and zero to be selected. Potentiometers are widely used in electronic circuits, as they allow precise adjustment of just the right amount of output voltage desired for the application.

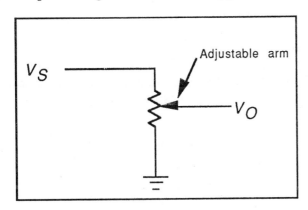

Figure 7–2

SUMMARY

In this experiment, you will build and demonstrate resistive voltage dividers and show the effect on the output voltage at various levels of loading. You will also demonstrate the use of a potentiometer as a variable voltage divider.

PROCEDURE

1. Refer to the voltage divider circuit in Figure 7–3. Calculate the output voltage with and without the 1 kΩ load.

$$V_O = \underline{\hspace{4cm}} \text{volts (1 k}\Omega \text{ load)}$$
$$V_O = \underline{\hspace{4cm}} \text{volts (no load)}$$

2. Connect the circuit shown in Figure 7–3. Do not connect the 1 kΩ resistor. Measure the output voltage across R_2. This is the no-load voltage.

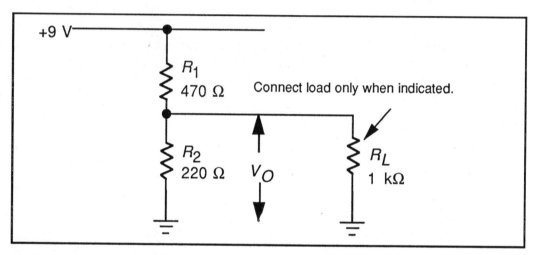

Figure 7–3

$$V_O = \underline{\hspace{4cm}} \text{volts}$$

3. Connect a 1 kΩ load resistor across R_2 as shown in Figure 7–3. Measure the output voltage with this load connected. Then remove the 1 kΩ load and replace it with a 10 kΩ resistor. Again measure the output voltage. Finally, replace the 10 kΩ resistor with a 100 kΩ resistor. Measure the output voltage. Record the output values in the table.

LOAD RESISTANCE (R_L)	OUTPUT VOLTAGE (V_O)
1 kΩ	
10 kΩ	
100 kΩ	

4. Based on the data you accumulated in step 3, how does the output voltage vary with different values of load resistance?

5. Disconnect the circuit in Figure 7–3. Mount the 10 kΩ potentiometer on your breadboarding socket. Each of the pins should go into a hole on a separate vertical column of holes on the breadboarding socket. The center pin is the variable arm. Then connect the 9-volt power supply to it as shown in Figure 7–4. You will measure the output voltage between the negative terminal of the battery and the arm of the potentiometer.

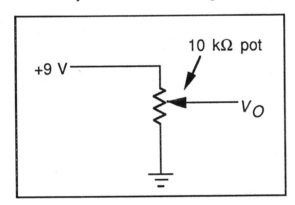

Figure 7–4

6. Connect your multimeter across the pot output as shown in Figure 7–4 to measure the output voltage (V_O). Adjust the potentiometer arm to the full counterclockwise (CCW) position with a small screwdriver. Note the output voltage. Then adjust the pot arm for a full clockwise (CW) position. Again, note the output voltage. Record your values.

V_O = _____ volts (CCW)
V_O = _____ volts (CW)

7. Now monitor the output voltage of the potentiometer. Adjust it for an output voltage of one half the input (power supply) voltage.

8. Disconnect the circuit.

DC Experiments

9. Using your multimeter, measure the resistance between the center lead (the arm) and each of the other leads. Record your values.

Resistance between center arm and one lead = _____ ohms

Resistance between center arm and other lead = _____ ohms

Explain the values you get.

10. Construct the voltage divider circuit shown in Figure 7–5. Calculate the range over which the output voltage can be varied with the pot.

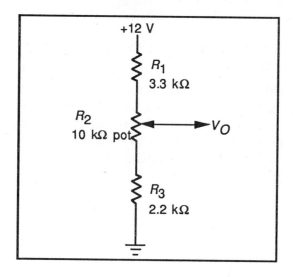

Figure 7–5

$V_O =$ _____ volts (CCW)

$V_O =$ _____ volts (CW)

11. Apply power to the circuit. Measure the output voltage while varying the pot over its full range. Record the voltage limits.

$V_O =$ _____ volts (CCW)

$V_O =$ _____ volts (CW)

REVIEW QUESTIONS

1. A voltage divider like the one in Figure 7–1 has resistor values R_1 = 10 kΩ and R_2 = 1kΩ. The source voltage is 15 volts. The output voltage is:

    a. 1.28 volts
    b. 1.36 volts
    c. 1.5 volts
    d. 1.72 volts

2. What is the minimum value of load resistance that can be connected to the voltage divider in question 1 without significantly lowering the output voltage?

    a. 100 ohms
    b. 1 kΩ
    c. 10 kΩ
    d. 100 kΩ

3. A variable voltage divider is a:

    a. pot
    b. variable resistor
    c. rheostat
    d. varistor

4. A DC voltage of 6 volts is applied across a pot. The output voltage can be set to any voltage between:

    a. −6 and +6
    b. 0 and 6
    c. 0 and 9
    d. 0 and 12

5. The pot in question 4 is set to tap off 85% of the applied voltage. The output is:

    a. .9 volts
    b. 2.6 volts
    c. 4.3 volts
    d. 5.1 volts

EXPERIMENT 8 ➤ Bridge Circuits

OBJECTIVES

When you complete this experiment, you will be able to identify, build, and balance a bridge circuit.

MATERIALS REQUIRED

- Digital multimeter
- Breadboarding socket
- DC power supply
- one—10 kΩ pot
- Resistors—¼ watt, 5%:
  one–4.7 kΩ
  one–12 kΩ
  one–18 kΩ
  one–100 kΩ

INTRODUCTION

A bridge circuit is a special connection of components that produces an output voltage which is balanced with respect to ground. It is widely used in measuring instruments and in a variety of industrial control circuits.

The basic bridge circuit is shown in Figure 8–1A. It is typically drawn in the diamond-shaped configuration to clearly identify it as a bridge circuit. But upon closer examination, you can see that the bridge circuit is basically two voltage dividers connected *across* the voltage source. The bridge circuit as shown in Figure 8–1B clearly shows this. Note that the output is taken from *between* the two voltage divider outputs.

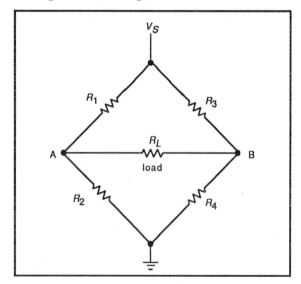

Figure 8–1A

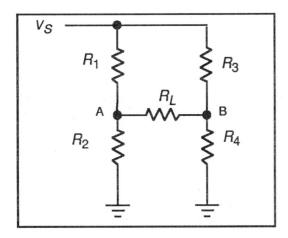

Figure 8–1B

Normally the output from a voltage divider is taken from the junction of the two resistors with respect to ground. In a bridge circuit, the output is taken from between the two voltage divider outputs and *not* with reference to ground. This kind of output is referred to as a balanced output.

BRIDGE BALANCE

The basic neutral condition in a bridge circuit is called *balance*. A balanced bridge is one in which the output voltage is zero. This occurs when the output voltage from one voltage divider is equal to the output of the other voltage divider, both with respect to ground. By making one or more of the resistive elements in the bridge variable, it is possible to adjust the bridge for this balanced state. Balance occurs when the following relationship is present:

$$R_1/R_2 = R_3/R_4$$

To repeat, if the ratios of the voltage divider resistors are equal, then the bridge is balanced and the output voltage is zero.

The bridge is unbalanced when one voltage divider output is higher or lower than the other. For example, in Figure 8–1 if the voltage at point A is greater than the voltage at point B, then A will be more positive than B. If that condition occurs, current will flow through the load from B to A.

If the bridge is unbalanced in the opposite direction and the voltage at B is greater than the voltage at A, the opposite will occur; current will flow through the load from A to B.

SUMMARY

In this experiment, you are going to build a bridge circuit and experiment with it. A potentiometer will be used in one of the arms of the bridge to achieve the various conditions just described.

DC Experiments

PROCEDURE

1. Refer to Figure 8–2. Values for R_1, R_2, and R_3 are given. R_4 is a 10 kΩ potentiometer connected as a variable resistor, which can be adjusted to any value between zero and 10 k ohms. Only two of the three connections on the pot will be used, the center variable arm and one other. Using the formula given for a balanced bridge, compute the value to which potentiometer R_4 must be set in order to balance the bridge. Rearrange the formula to solve for R_4 and record your value.

$$R_4 = \underline{\hspace{4cm}} \text{ ohms}$$

2. Construct the circuit shown in Figure 8–2. Adjust R_4 for the middle of its range as a starting point.

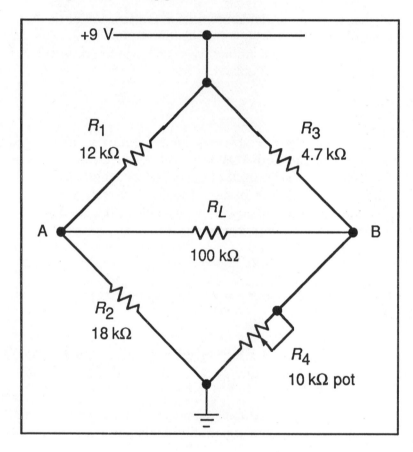

Figure 8–2

3. Connect your multimeter between terminals A and B to read voltage. You should read some value of voltage. Adjust the range switch on the multimeter for maximum resolution.

4. Now, adjust potentiometer R_4 until the voltage between A and B is zero. When you obtain a zero reading, switch the multimeter to the next *lowest* voltage setting. You may notice some residual voltage. In this case continue to fine tune the adjustment of the potentiometer until a zero reading is obtained. This is the balanced setting of the bridge.

5. With the bridge in the balanced condition, measure the voltage at point A with respect to ground (the negative terminal of the power supply) and at point B with respect to ground. Record your values.

$$V_A = \text{_____} \text{ volts}$$

$$V_B = \text{_____} \text{ volts}$$

6. Remove the potentiometer R_4 from the breadboard. Do this carefully so as not to disturb the setting. Once you have removed it, measure the resistance between the two terminals you connected to the bridge circuit. Record your resistance value.

$$R_4 = \text{_____} \text{ ohms}$$

7. Compare your calculated and measured value of R_4 for a balanced bridge condition.

8. Reconnect the potentiometer in the bridge circuit. Be sure to plug the pot leads into the same holes. Measure the voltage between A and B to be sure that it is still zero. If it is not, readjust R_4 as necessary to bring the bridge into a balanced condition.

9. While monitoring the voltage between terminals A and B, vary the potentiometer in both the clockwise and counterclockwise positions from the point where the bridge is balanced. Note the amplitude and polarity of the voltage as you vary the potentiometer. Record the amplitude and polarity of the voltage at the maximum counterclockwise and maximum clockwise positions of R_4.

Output voltage = _____ volts (max. CCW)

Output voltage = _____ volts (max. CW)

10. Disconnect the circuit.

REVIEW QUESTIONS

1. When a bridge is balanced, the output voltage is:

   a. the supply voltage
   b. not possible to determine
   c. infinite
   d. zero

2. A bridge circuit is made up of two simpler circuits of what type?

   a. Voltage dividers
   b. Series
   c. Parallel
   d. Current dividers

3. In the bridge circuit of Figure 8–1, the voltage between A and ground is +7.5. The voltage from B to ground is +4.6. Current will flow in the load in what direction?

   a. left to right
   b. right to left
   c. no current will flow

4. In a bridge like Figure 8–1, R_1 is unknown, $R_2 = 1$ kΩ, $R_3 = 3$ kΩ, $R_4 = 8$ kΩ. What is the value of R_1 to balance the bridge?

   a. 375 ohms
   b. 1.25 k ohms
   c. 2.4 k ohms
   d. 2.67 k ohms

5. One output terminal of a bridge is connected to ground.

   a. True
   b. False

EXPERIMENT 9 ➤ Temperature Sensitive Resistors

OBJECTIVES

When you complete this experiment, you will be able to predict the operation of circuits containing temperature-sensitive resistors.

MATERIALS REQUIRED

- Digital multimeter
- Breadboarding socket
- DC power supply
- Soldering iron
- Components
  one–1 kΩ NTC thermistor
  one–1 kΩ, ¼ watt, 5% resistor

INTRODUCTION

All electrical conductors are sensitive to temperature variations. An ordinary copper wire has a positive temperature coefficient; as it gets hotter, its resistance increases. However, the *percentage* of resistance increase is very small. In most applications, excessive heat will not affect the resistance of a wire significantly.

On the other hand, there are types of resistances that experience a large variation in resistance for relatively small temperature changes. Such devices are useful in a number of applications.

OTHER RESISTORS

NTC Thermistor

A special resistor designed for large resistance changes with temperature fluctuations is known as a thermistor. Thermistors typically have a *negative* temperature coefficient (NTC). This means that as their temperature increases, their resistance decreases and vice versa. A significant resistance change occurs even over a narrow temperature change. These sensors are used to build anything from electronic thermometers to detectors in certain industrial control systems where temperature *must* be monitored and/or controlled.

PTC Thermistor

Positive temperature coefficient (PTC) thermistors are also available. These devices increase in resistance for an increase in temperature. Their resistance increase is more abrupt and steeper than a negative temperature coefficient thermistor.

A good example of a resistor with a positive temperature coefficient is the filament of a light bulb. When the light bulb is off, the filament has a very low resistance value. But when current is applied to the bulb, the filament glows brightly and rapidly heats to a white hot temperature. This significantly increases the *resistance* of the filament. For example, a standard 100-watt bulb has a cold resistance of about 10 ohms. But when it has 120 volts applied to it, it heats up to a resistance of 144 ohms, an increase of 14.4 times. The characteristics of a light bulb can be used to provide regulation in some types of electrical and electronic circuits.

SUPERCONDUCTIVITY

There is an extreme case of resistance variation with temperature. That is when the resistance drops to zero after the temperature is reduced to a very low level. Certain materials actually *lose* all resistance when their temperature is lowered to a value just above absolute zero ($-273°$ C). This phenomenon is known as superconductivity. On-going research seeks new materials whose resistance is eliminated at much higher temperatures, thus making them more practical.

SUMMARY

In this experiment you will work with a thermistor to demonstrate its temperature-sensitive characteristics.

PROCEDURE

1. Prepare two cups or glasses of water. You will use them to change the temperature of a thermistor. Fill one glass with very hot water from the tap. Fill another glass with cold water and add ice cubes.

2. Identify the thermistor. As you can see, it is a circular disk of special resistance material. It is ¼" in diameter with wire leads soldered to each side of it. First, take the thermistor and measure its resistance at room temperature with your multimeter.

    $R =$ _____ ohms (room temperature)

3. Hold the multimeter probes on the thermistor leads with your fingers and dip the thermistor body into the hot water. Wait about 10 seconds and note the resistance.

    $R =$ _____ ohms (hot)

4. Remove the thermistor from the warm water and immediately insert it into the glass of cold water. Again, note the resistance after 10 seconds.

    $R =$ _____ ohms (cold)

5. Based on the results obtained in the two previous steps, write a statement about how the resistance changes with variations in temperature.

6. Build the circuit shown in Figure 9–1. Note that the thermistor is connected with a 1 kΩ resistor as part of a voltage divider across a 9-volt power supply. Remember that the output voltage is taken from *across* the thermistor. Measure the output voltage at room temperature.

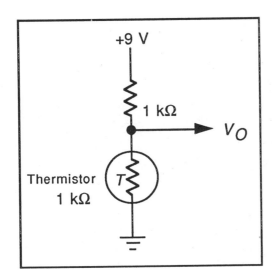

Figure 9–1

$V_O =$ _____ volts (room temperature)

7. Heat a soldering iron and bring it approximately ¼ inch from the thermistor. Allow it to heat the thermistor while you observe the voltage change across the thermistor. After a period of 10 seconds, record the voltage value.

$V_O =$ _____ volts (heated)

Be sure to allow the thermistor to cool before you proceed to step 8.

8. Modify the experimental circuit so that it appears like that shown in Figure 9–2. Again, you are using the thermistor as part of a voltage divider. But, in this circuit, the output voltage is taken from across the 1 kΩ resistor rather than across the thermistor. Measure and record the output voltage across the 1 kΩ resistor at room temperature.

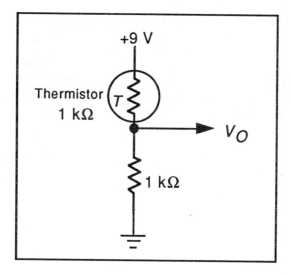

Figure 9–2

$V_O =$ _____ volts (room temperature)

9. Again, bring the soldering iron to within ¼ inch of the thermistor and allow it to heat. Monitor the voltage across the 1 kΩ resistor for approximately 10 seconds and note how the voltage changes. At the end of 10 seconds, record the voltage.

$V_O =$ _____ volts (heated)

10. How does the output voltage vary with temperature in each circuit?

REVIEW QUESTIONS

1. Positive temperature coefficient means that as:

   a. temperature decreases, resistance decreases
   b. temperature increases, resistance decreases
   c. temperature decreases, resistance increases
   d. temperature varies, resistance changes

2. In a light bulb, the hot resistance is lower than the cold resistance.

   a. True
   b. False

3. The total loss of resistance at very low temperatures is known as:

   a. super-resistance
   b. extreme temperature coefficient
   c. superconductivity
   d. cold resistance

4. To convert the resistance change of a thermistor into a voltage variation, it is connected in which type of circuit?

    a. Amplifier
    b. Counter
    c. Filter
    d. Voltage divider

5. Thermistors are sometimes used in bridge circuits.

    a. True
    b. False

EXPERIMENT 10 ➤ Power in Resistive Circuits

OBJECTIVES

When you complete this experiment, you will be able to determine the amount of power dissipated in a resistance and express the relationship between load resistance and internal source resistance for maximum power transfer.

MATERIALS REQUIRED

- Digital multimeter
- Breadboarding socket
- DC power supply
- Resistors—¼ watt, 5%:
    one–120
    one–150
    one–220
    one–470
    two–1 kΩ
    one–2.2 kΩ
    one–4.7 kΩ
    one–10 kΩ

INTRODUCTION

To explain at a very basic level, electrical power is dissipated in resistance. Whenever current flows through a resistance, power is generated. That power is released as heat. At low power levels, a small amount of heat is produced. As higher currents are used, more power is dissipated and high heat levels are generated. That's why many electronic components actually run "hot."

Most electronic components are designed to withstand only a certain maximum amount of power. This goes for resistors, transistors, and other devices. For example, standard composition and film resistors are available in power ratings of ⅛, ¼, ½, 1, and 2 watts. The higher the power rating, the larger is the size of the resistor to safely dissipate that power. Also, the wattage rating of a resistor states the *maximum* amount of power that a resistor can dissipate safely.

DESIGNING CIRCUITS

When designing electronic circuits, it is necessary to calculate the amount of power dissipated by the resistor to ensure that it is below the maximum rating. If it is not, the resistor will literally burn up. To illustrate, a ¼-watt resistor must have values of current and voltage such that the total power dissipation is less than that wattage.

POWER FORMULAS

Power can be calculated with three basic formulas. These formulas are:

$$P = VI$$
$$P = I^2R$$
$$P = V^2/R$$

Select the formula based upon the values of current, voltage or resistance available to you.

TRANSFERRING POWER—SOURCE TO LOAD

In electrical and electronic systems, it is desirable to transfer as much power from the voltage source to the load as possible. The maximum transfer of power from a generator, battery, power supply or other electronic circuit to a load occurs when the load is matched to the internal resistance of the generator, Figure 10–1.

In this figure, a battery is connected in series with a resistor, which we will refer to as the internal resistance R_i. The load to which the power will be applied is designated as R_L. In order for maximum power to be transferred *to* the load, the load resistance must be equal to the internal resistance of the generator. In Figure 10–1, assuming R_L is 1,000 ohms and R_i is 1,000 ohms, maximum power will be delivered to the load.

But, since the two resistances are equal, then half the power will be *dissipated* in each. This means that when maximum power transfer occurs, the same amount of power is dissipated in the source as in the load. This represents an efficiency of only 50%, but maximum power dissipation occurs only under this condition.

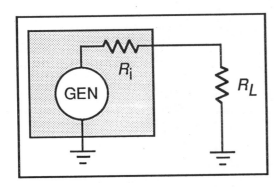

Figure 10–1

SUMMARY

In this experiment, you are going to see the effect of power dissipation in a resistance. You will actually show that heat is produced. Further, you will also demonstrate the conditions under which maximum power transfer takes place.

PROCEDURE

1. Refer to the simple circuit shown in Figure 10–2. Given the values of voltage and resistance shown, compute and record the amount of power dissipated by the resistor.

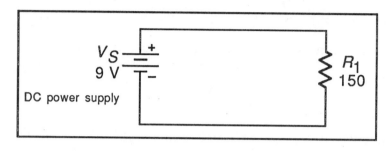

Figure 10–2

$P =$ _____ watts

2. Connect the circuit shown in Figure 10–2. After a few seconds, touch the resistor quickly to feel any heat build-up, but be careful. The resistor can get extremely hot. Leave the resistor connected for a few minutes and note the effect that the current through it has. Given that most of the resistors used in a school lab are ¼-watt units, has the wattage rating of this resistor been exceeded?

3. Construct the circuit shown in Figure 10–3. A 1 kΩ resistor is used to simulate the internal resistance of a 9-volt generator represented by the power supply. In step 4 you will connect various values of resistance as the load and determine the amount of power dissipated in each case.

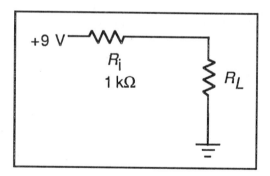

Figure 10–3

4. Listed in the following table are the values of resistance you will use for the load. Beginning with the lowest value, connect it to the circuit you just constructed. Measure the voltage across the resistance and then compute the amount of power dissipated. Repeat this step with each of the resistor values given and fill in the spaces in the table.

LOAD RESISTANCE (R_L)	LOAD VOLTAGE	LOAD POWER (P)
120		
220		
470		
1 kΩ		
2.2 kΩ		
4.7 kΩ		
10 kΩ		

5. Refer to your data in the table. Note which load resistance value produces the greatest amount of power dissipation.

$$R_L = \underline{\hspace{3cm}} \text{ ohms}$$

6. How does it compare to the internal impedance of the generator?

7. Disconnect the circuit and put away all of your components.

REVIEW QUESTIONS

1. The power dissipated in a resistor with 12 volts across it and .15 A through it is:

   a. 1.25 watts
   b. 1.8 watts
   c. 12.5 watts
   d. 80 watts

2. Current in a 22 ohm resistor is 3 A. The power dissipated is:

   a. 7.3 watts
   b. 22 watts
   c. 66 watts
   d. 198 watts

3. A 4.7 k ohm, ¼ watt resistor has 40 volts across it. The power rating has been exceeded.

    a. True
    b. False

4. Power is dissipated as:

    a. light
    b. an electric field
    c. heat
    d. a magnetic field

5. A radio transmitter has an output resistance of 50 ohms. Its load is an antenna. The antenna resistance for maximum power output should be:

    a. 25 ohms
    b. 50 ohms
    c. 100 ohms
    d. 150 ohms

EXPERIMENT 11 ➤ Thevenin's Theorem

OBJECTIVE

When you complete this experiment, you will be able to demonstrate and verify Thevenin's theorem and use it to analyze circuits.

MATERIALS REQUIRED

- Multimeter
- Breadboarding socket
- DC power supply
- Resistors—¼ watt, 5%:
  one–470 ohm resistor
  one–1 kΩ resistor
  one–2.2 kΩ resistor
  one–3.3 kΩ resistor

INTRODUCTION

Thevenin's theorem is a circuit analysis technique that greatly facilitates the analysis and design of circuits. It permits you to replace complex circuitry between a voltage source and a load with a single series resistor. For example, assume that you wish to analyze the performance of the circuit in Figure 11-1.

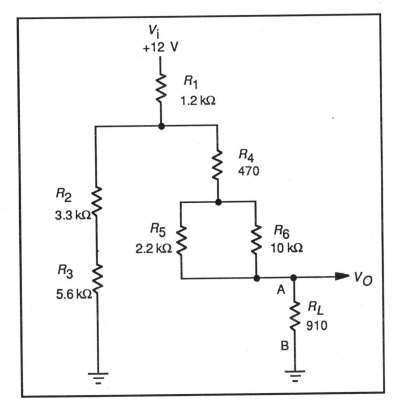

Figure 11–1

THE PROBLEM

Specifically, you wish to know the load or output voltage for different values of load resistance, R_L. Each time you change R_L, you have to find the total resistance and current, branch currents, and voltage drops. The process is not difficult, but it is tedious and time consuming.

THE SOLUTION

By using Thevenin's theorem, all of the circuitry between the voltage source and the load can be replaced by a single series resistor value called the Thevenin's *equivalent resistance*, R_{TH}. The voltage source is replaced with a difference value voltage source called the Thevenin's *equivalent voltage*, V_{TH}, Figure 11–2.

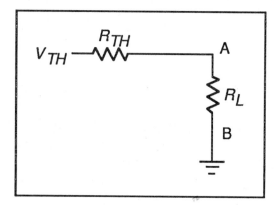

Figure 11–2

Together, the Thevenin's equivalent voltage and resistance will produce the same voltage *across* and current *in* any load as the original circuit. Circuit analysis is now much easier, since the problem has been reduced to a simple series circuit.

THE STEPS

The easiest way to determine the Thevenin equivalents is to measure them in the actual circuit. To do this in Figure 11–1, remove the load and, with the source voltage applied, measure the voltage between the load terminals A and B. This is the Thevenin's equivalent voltage V_{TH}.

Next, with the load still removed, disconnect the source voltage and replace it with a short. Then measure the resistance between load terminals A and B. This is the Thevenin's equivalent resistance R_{TH}.

You can then actually build the Thevenin's equivalent circuit with a variable voltage source set to V_{TH} and select the closest standard resistor to R_{TH}. Now you can connect different loads and see how they work.

CIRCUIT VALUES

The other approach is to calculate V_{TH} and R_{TH} from the circuit values. First, remove the load resistor R_L and calculate the voltage appearing at terminals A and B. For the circuit in Figure 11–1, removing R_7 leaves R_4, R_5, and R_6 open. As a result, the voltage across R_2 and R_3 appears between A and B.

$$V_{TH} = V_{AB} = 12(R_2 + R_3)/(R_1 + R_2 + R_3)$$

$$V_{TH} = V_{AB} = 12(8.9 \text{ k}\Omega/10.1) = 12(.881) = 10.6 \text{ V}$$

Next, R_{TH} is computed. With R_7 removed, the 12-volt supply is replaced with a short. The resistance between A and B is computed.

$$\frac{1.2 \text{ k}\Omega (8.9 \text{ k}\Omega)}{(1.2 \text{ k}\Omega + 8.9 \text{ k}\Omega)} = \frac{10.68 \text{ k}\Omega}{10.1 \text{ k}\Omega} = 1.06 \text{ k}\Omega$$

R_4 in series with R_5–R_6 in parallel:

$$1.8 \text{ k}\Omega + 4.7 \text{ k}\Omega = 2.27 \text{ k}\Omega$$

Total resistance between A and B:

$$2.27 \text{ k}\Omega + 1.06 \text{ k}\Omega = 3.33 \text{ k}\Omega$$

The Thevenin's equivalent is a DC voltage source of 10.6 volts in series with a resistance of 3.33 kΩ.

Connecting R_7 to this, there is now a total resistance of:

$$910 + 3330 = 4240 \text{ ohms}$$

The total current is:

$$10/4240 = .0024 \text{ A} = 2.4 \text{ mA}$$

And the voltage across R_7 is:

$$10.6(910/910 + 3330) = 10.6(910/4240) = 2.28 \text{ volts}$$

SUMMARY

You will use this procedure in the experiment that follows.

PROCEDURE

1. Refer to the circuit in Figure 11–3. Using the values shown, calculate the Thevenin's equivalent voltage and resistance at terminals A and B. Calculate the output voltage across a load resistance of 3.3 kilohms.

$$V_{TH} = \text{_____} \text{ volts}$$
$$R_{TH} = \text{_____} \text{ volts}$$
$$V_L = \text{_____} \text{ volts}$$

2. Construct the circuit in Figure 11–3. Apply power and measure the Thevenin's equivalent output voltage across A and B with no load.

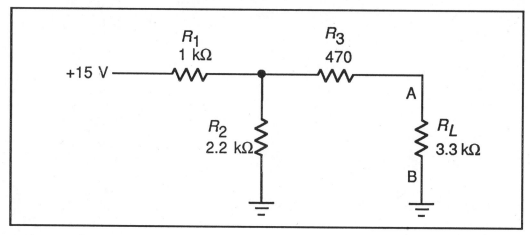

Figure 11–3

$$V_{TH} \text{ (measured)} = \text{_____} \text{ volts}$$

3. Apply the 3.3 kilohm load to A and B. Measure the output voltage. How does it compare to your calculated value?

$$V_L \text{ (measured)} = \text{_____} \text{ volts}$$

4. Turn off the power. Disconnect the power supply. In its place, install a wire short. Also disconnect the load from terminals A and B. Then measure the Thevenin's equivalent resistance at terminals A and B with an ohmmeter.

$$R_{TH} \text{ (measured)} = \text{_____} \text{ volts}$$

5. Draw the Thevenin's equivalent circuit and label the values. Then build the circuit using the power supply and a resistor. Use the closest standard resistor value available.

6. Turn on the power and the measure the Thevenin's output voltage. Adjust the power supply to the value you calculated in step 1.

7. Connect the 3.3 kilohm load to the equivalent circuit and measure the output voltage. Is it the same as that you measured in step 3? Explain.

REVIEW QUESTIONS

1. In Figure 11–1, with R_7 removed, why doesn't the resistive combination R_4–R_5–R_6 affect the output voltage?

   a. Actually, they do affect output voltage.
   b. No current flows or voltage drops appear in them.
   c. The resistance of this combination is much smaller than R_7, so does not affect the output.

2. What values of load resistance would produce maximum load power?

   a. 910
   b. 1.06 kΩ
   c. 3.33 kΩ
   d. 10.6 kΩ

3. To compute V_{TH}, R_L is:

   a. removed or open
   b. shorted

4. To compute R_{TH}, the source voltage is:

   a. opened
   b. shorted

5. Thevenin's theorem works with AC as well as DC.

   a. True
   b. False

EXPERIMENT 12 ➤ Superposition Theorem

OBJECTIVE

When you complete this experiment, you will be able to analyze circuits using the superposition theorem.

MATERIALS REQUIRED

- Multimeter
- Breadboarding socket
- Two independent, adjustable DC power supplies
- Resistors—¼ watt, 5%:
  one–1 kΩ resistor
  one–1.5 kΩ resistor
  one–2.2 kΩ resistor

INTRODUCTION

Superposition is a technique used to analyze complete circuits using two or more voltage sources. While loop, mesh, and modal analysis can also be used to analyze such circuits, the superposition theorem is a much faster and easier method.

To use the superposition theorem for analysis follow three steps:

1. replace all voltage sources except one with a short, then calculate all currents and voltage drops;

2. replace that voltage source with a short and recompute the circuit after reconnecting one other voltage source; and

3. algebraically add all currents from your calculations and compute all voltage drops. An example is given in Figure 12–1.

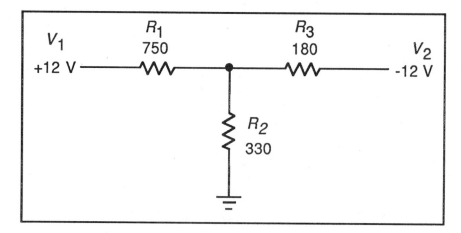

Figure 12–1

EXAMPLE STEPS

Step 1.

The goal is to compute the voltage across R_2. First, V_2 is replaced with a short. This puts R_2 and R_3 in parallel. Their equivalent resistance is:

$$180(330)/(180 + 330) = 59400/510 = 116.5 \text{ ohms}$$

The total resistance is:

$$116.5 + 750 = 866.5 \text{ ohms}$$

The total current drawn from the +12 volts supply is:

$$12/866.5 = .01385 \text{ A} = 13.85 \text{ mA}$$

The voltage drop across R_1 is:

$$.01385(750) = 10.39 \text{ volts}$$

The voltage across R_2 and R_3 is:

$$12 - 10.39 = 1.61 \text{ volts}$$

The current in R_2 is:

$$1.61/330 = .0049 \text{ A} = 4.88 \text{ mA}$$

The current in R_3 is:

$$1.61/180 = .00894 \text{ A} = 8.94 \text{ mA}$$

Step 2.

Next, V_1 is replaced with a short. This puts R_1 in parallel with R_2. The equivalent resistance of R_1 and R_2 is:

$$[750(330)/750 + 330] = 247500/1080 = 229.2 \text{ ohms}$$

The total resistance is:

$$229.2 + R_3 = 229.2 + 180 = 409.2 \text{ ohms}$$

The total circuit current is:

$$12/409.2 = .02933 \text{ A} = 29.33 \text{ mA}$$

The voltage drop of R_3 is:

$$.02933(180) = 5.28 \text{ volts}$$

The voltage across R_1 and R_2 is:

$$12 - 5.28 = 6.72 \text{ volts}$$

The current in R_1 is:

$$6.72/750 = .00896 = 8.96 \text{ mA}$$

The current in R_2 is:

$$6.72/330 = .02036 \text{ A} = 20.36 \text{ mA}$$

Step 3.

Now the total current in R_2 can be found by adding the currents you just calculated. The current in R_2 caused by V_2 is 20.36 mA and flows from top to bottom (electron flow). The current in R_2 caused by V_1 is 4.88 mA and flows from bottom to top. Since the two currents are opposing, the net current when both supplies are connected is their difference.

$$20.36 - 4.88 = 15.48 \text{ mA}$$

The direction of flow is that of the larger current (from top to bottom).

The voltage across R_2 then is:

$$.01548(330) = 5.1 \text{ volts}$$

That voltage is negative with respect to ground (-5.1 volts).

SUMMARY

You will demonstrate this procedure in the steps that follow.

PROCEDURE

1. Refer to the circuit in Figure 12–2. Use the superposition theorem to calculate all of the currents and voltage drops in the circuit. Show your work. What is the voltage across R_2 and its polarity?

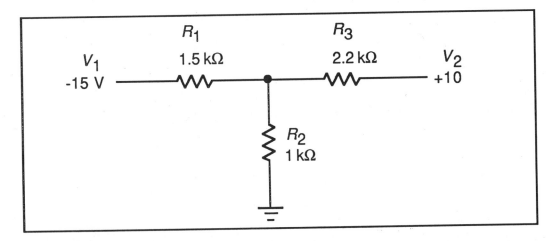

Figure 12–2

$$V_{R_2} = \underline{\hspace{4cm}} \text{ volts}$$

2. Make a table showing all of your calculated values as produced by source V_1 alone, source V_2 alone, and with sources V_1 and V_2 connected at the same time.

3. Wire the circuit shown in Figure 12–2. For this step, do not connect V_2. Instead, install a wire short where V_2 is shown.

4. Apply power. Set V_1 to –15 volts. Measure all of the resistor currents and voltage drops. Record them in your table.

5. Turn off the power. Disconnect the wire short and, in its place connect V_2. Disconnect V_1 and install a wire short in its place.

6. Turn on the power. Set V_2 for +10 volts. Measure all of the currents and voltage drops. Record them in your table.

7. Turn the power off. Disconnect the wire short and reconnect V_1.

8. Turn the power back on. Now, measure all of the currents and voltages with both sources connected. Again, record the data in your table. What is the voltage across R_2? Give the polarity.

$$V_{R_2} = \underline{\hspace{4cm}} \text{ volts}$$

DC Experiments

REVIEW QUESTIONS

1. Superposition theorem is usually easier to use than mesh or nodal analysis.

   a. True
   b. False

2. Superposition theorem is used to analyze circuits with one voltage source.

   a. True
   b. False

3. What is the polarity of the voltage drop across R_2 in Figure 12–2 if both supply polarities are reversed?

   a. Negative
   b. Positive

4. The voltage drop across R_1 in Figure 12–2 is:

   a. 2.56
   b. 7.44
   c. 12.44
   d. 25.44

5. The voltage drop across R_3 in Figure 12–2 is:

   a. 2.56
   b. 8.44
   c. 12.44
   d. 7.44

EXPERIMENT 13 ➤ Inductors and DC

OBJECTIVE

When you complete this experiment, you will be able to demonstrate and state the effect of inductance in a DC circuit.

MATERIALS REQUIRED

- Digital multimeter
- DC power supply (9 to 15 volts)
- Power transformer
- Neon bulb (NE-2) with wire leads

INTRODUCTION

Inductance is the property of an electronic component that opposes changes in current through it. Inductance is exhibited by components known as inductors, coils or chokes. If the current flowing in an inductor changes, the property of inductance will oppose the change. If the current increases, the inductor will oppose the increase. If the current decreases, the inductor will again attempt to maintain the current.

The effect of inductance is primarily noticeable in those circuits where alternating current is used. The opposition to AC exhibited by an inductor is referred to as *inductive reactance*. Like resistance, inductive reactance produces a fixed opposition that controls the current level in a circuit.

In DC circuits, since the current is usually a fixed value determined by the resistance and voltage, inductors would appear to have little or no effect. However, they do affect DC and it is important to understand this phenomenon.

INDUCTORS IN DC CIRCUITS

The primary purpose of an inductor in a DC circuit is to offer opposition in the form of resistance. Inductors are coils made of wire that create resistance. While the resistance of an inductor is usually low, it does offer opposition. In addition, power is dissipated by the resistance of the inductor.

The effects of inductance show up when the current in a DC circuit changes. While the current is typically fixed in an operating DC circuit, remember that it is necessary to turn the circuit off and on. When current is first applied to or removed from the circuit, a significant change takes place. This change in current causes the inductor to oppose the change. The result is an induced voltage which, as in the AC circuit, opposes the current change.

The most dramatic effect is that produced when the current through an inductor is suddenly removed. The magnetic field around the inductor collapses, inducing a very high voltage in the coil. This voltage can be damaging to components in some applications. Other applications take advantage of this effect to produce a very high voltage to power special components or circuits. Examples are fly-back transformers in TV sets and induction coils in auto ignition systems.

SUMMARY

In this experiment, you will demonstrate the effects of an inductor in a DC circuit.

PROCEDURE

1. For this experiment, you will use the primary winding of a transformer. This winding is identified by two black leads. Ignore all other leads. Measure the resistance of the inductor. Record the value.

    DC resistance = _____ ohms

2. Predict what the current might be if a 15-volt power supply is applied to the inductor.

    Current = _____ mA

3. Connect a 15-volt power supply to the inductor and measure the direct current flowing in it. Refer to Figure 13–1. Record the amount of current flowing.

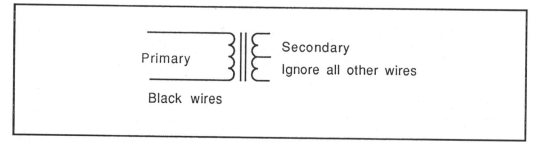

Figure 13–1   Primary Winding Used as Inductor

    Measured current = _____ mA

4. What effect does the battery have on the inductor and what effect does the inductor have on the current in the circuit?

5. Locate the neon bulb. This is a small glass lamp with thin wire leads. Connect the neon lamp in parallel with the inductor as shown in Figure 13–2. The neon lamp will glow only if the voltage across it exceeds about 70 to 90 volts.

6. Apply 15 volts from a power supply to the inductor as Figure 13-2 shows. Note the condition of the bulb. Is the bulb on or off?

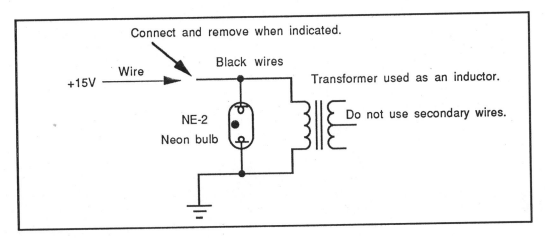

Connect and remove when indicated.

Black wires

+15V — Wire →

Transformer used as an inductor.

NE-2
Neon bulb

Do not use secondary wires.

Figure 13-2

Bulb condition = _____

7. Disconnect one lead of the power supply from the inductor and again note the condition of the bulb.

Bulb condition = _____

8. Repeat steps 6 and 7 several times to be sure you see what is happening.

9. Explain the action that occurred in steps 7 and 8.

REVIEW QUESTIONS

1. An inductor opposes changes in:

   a. voltage
   b. current
   c. resistance
   d. inductance

2. Another name for an inductor is:

   a. transformer
   b. magnet
   c. solenoid
   d. choke

3. All coils have resistance.

    a. True
    b. False

4. The opposition to DC offered by an inductor is called:

    a. inductance
    b. resistance
    c. reactance
    d. impedance

5. A voltage of 30 volts is applied to a 90-volt neon bulb. The bulb will be:

    a. on
    b. off

EXPERIMENT 14 ➤ RC Time Constant

OBJECTIVE

When you complete this experiment, you will be able to demonstrate how the values of capacitance and resistance control the charge and discharge time of a capacitor.

MATERIALS REQUIRED

- Digital multimeter
- Breadboarding socket
- DC power supply
- Stop watch or watch with sweep second hand
- Components
  one–22 µF electrolytic capacitor
  one–100 µF electrolytic capacitor
  one–33 kΩ, ¼-watt resistor
  one–100 kΩ, ¼-watt resistor
  one–220 kΩ, ¼-watt resistor
  one–1 megohm, ¼-watt resistor

INTRODUCTION

A *capacitor is an electronic component that stores electricity in the form of an electric field.* When a DC voltage is applied to a capacitor, electrons are pulled off one plate of the capacitor and piled up on the other plate because of the external voltage force. This produces a charge on the capacitor equal to the applied voltage. The positive charge on one plate of the capacitor and the negative charge on the other plate causes a strong electric field to be developed between the plates in the dielectric. This charge will be retained even if the voltage source is removed. The capacitor can be discharged by connecting the leads together to neutralize the charge on the plates.

The charging and discharging of the capacitor (called a time constant) to a DC voltage takes a finite amount of time; it depends basically upon the value of the capacitor and any series resistance. The charge time constant is the time that it takes the capacitor to charge to 63.2% of the applied voltage. That time (t) in seconds is equal to:

$$T = RC$$

The discharge time constant is the amount of time that it takes a capacitor to discharge to 36.8% of the initial charge.

The amount of time that it takes a capacitor to completely charge to the applied voltage or be completely discharged to zero is equal to approximately five time constants or 5 T.

SUMMARY

Many electronic circuits rely upon the concept of time constant for their operation. These include time delay, pulse and waveform shaping, and oscillator circuits. In this experiment, you will demonstrate the charge and discharge time constant, using three different groups of resistors and capacitors.

PROCEDURE

CHARGING ACTION

Resistor = 100 kΩ: Capacitor = 100 μF.

1. Construct the circuit shown in Figure 14–1. Observe the polarity of the electrolytic capacitor.

2. Set the DC voltage to 12 volts.

3. Calculate the amount of voltage that will appear on the capacitor after one time constant.

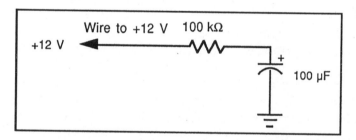

Figure 14–1

Voltage (T) = _____ volts

4. Calculate the time constant using the values shown in Figure 14–1. Record your value in column 3 of Figure 14–2.

   Also calculate the amount of time that it takes for the capacitor to become fully charged (5 T). Record your value in column 4 of Figure 14–2.

Column 1	Column 2	Column 3	Column 4	Column 5	Column 6
R	C	T (calc)	$5\,T$ (calc)	T (meas)	$5\,T$ (meas)
100 kΩ	100 µF				
100 kΩ	22 µF				
220 kΩ	100 µF				

Figure 14–2

5. Touch the probes of your multimeter across the capacitor with the correct polarity orientation. The reading should be zero volt. If not, it means that there is a residual charge on the capacitor. Remove it by temporarily shorting the capacitor leads together for a few seconds. Again, make the measurement with your voltmeter to be sure that the capacitor voltage is zero.

6. Leaving the multimeter probes across the capacitor, connect the free end of the 100 kilohm resistor to the +12 volt terminal of the battery or power supply. The instant you make the connection, start your stop watch or begin timing with the second hand of your watch. As the voltage on the capacitor begins to rise, make note of the voltage. When the voltage across the capacitor reaches the value you computed in step 2, note the time on the stop watch or second hand. Record this value as the measured time constant in column 5 of Figure 14–2.

   NOTE: You may wish to repeat this step several times to be sure that your timing is relatively accurate. You are attempting to watch both the voltmeter reading and the stop watch indication to determine the time that it takes for a specific voltage level to be reached. This is a tricky operation at best, so repeat it several times for greater accuracy. **IMPORTANT:** if you need to repeat the experiment, remove the 100 kilohm resistor and discharge the 100 µF capacitor completely before making each additional measurement.

7. Again, discharge the capacitor completely and reconnect the probes. Touch the free lead of the 100 kilohm resistor to the +12 volt terminal on the power supply. This time, measure the amount of time that it takes for the capacitor to fully charge to the value of the applied voltage you measured in step 1. As before, begin your timing with stop watch or sweep second hand the moment you apply the voltage to the resistor. Record the measured amount of time it takes for a full charge to be reached in the 5A column in Figure 14–2.

Resistor = 11 kΩ: Capacitor = 22 µF.

8. Repeat steps 4 through 7 using a 22 µF capacitor and 100 kilohm resistor. Fill in the blanks in Figure 14–2 as you did before with your calculated and measured values.

Resistor = 220 kΩ: Capacitor = 100 µF.

9. Again, repeat steps 4 through 7 but this time use a 100 µF capacitor and a 220 kilohm resistor. Record your calculated and measured values in the table of Figure 14–2.

OBSERVATION

10. Observing the information in Figure 14–2 and noting the different times obtained with different values of resistance and capacitance, draw your own conclusion about the effect of the resistance and capacitor values on the time constant.

DISCHARGING ACTION

Resistor = 100 kΩ: Capacitor = 100 µF.

11. Rewire the circuit so that it is like that shown in Figure 14–3. In this part of the experiment, you will demonstrate the discharge action of a capacitor. To do this, you will connect a resistor directly across the capacitor.

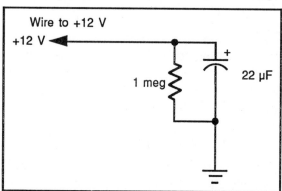

Figure 14–3

12. Calculate the circuit time constant and the time required for full discharge and record this data in column 3 of Figure 14–4.

Column 1	Column 2	Column 3	Column 4	Column 5	Column 6
R	C	T (calc)	$5\ T$(calc)	T (meas)	$5\ T$ (meas)
100 kΩ	100 µF				
100 kΩ	22 µF				
220 kΩ	100 µF				

Figure 14–4

13. Next, determine the amount of voltage to which the capacitor will discharge in one time constant. Use the original power supply voltage you measured in step 1. Calculate the amount of voltage that will be across the capacitor after discharging for one time constant.

Voltage (t) = _____ volts

Resistor = 100 kΩ: Capacitor = 22 µF.

14. Connect your voltmeter probes across the 22 µF capacitor. The voltage should be zero at this time, because any charge on the capacitor will have been removed by discharge through the 1 megohm resistor.

Connect the +12 volt terminal of the power supply to the circuit. The capacitor will immediately charge to the supply voltage; there is no resistance in series with the capacitor.

15. Continue to hold the probes of the voltmeter across the capacitor. Remove the hook-up wire from the +12 volt terminal on the power supply. Simultaneously, begin timing with your stop watch or sweep second hand. Observe the voltage across the capacitor. When the correct voltage occurs, note the time. Record the time constant in Column 5 of Figure 14–4.

As before, you may wish to repeat steps 13 and 14 several times to improve your accuracy. Since you are observing two values simultaneously, measurement is tricky. By averaging several readings, you will obtain greater accuracy in measurement.

Resistor = 220 kΩ: Capacitor = 22 µF.

16. Repeat steps 12 through 15 but use a 220 kilohm resistor and the 22 µF capacitor. Again, compute the discharge times for one time constant and five time constants. Record all of your data in Figure 14–4.

OBSERVATION

17. Observing the data in Figure 14–3, make a determination about the relationship between the time for discharge and the values of resistance and capacitance.

18. As you compare your calculated and measured values, explain any discrepancies.

REVIEW QUESTIONS

1. It takes the same amount of time for a capacitor to fully charge as it does to fully discharge.

   a. True
   b. False

2. To what voltage will a 5 µF capacitor charge through a 10 kilohm resistor in one time constant when connected to 6 volts?

   a. 1.4 volts
   b. 2.5 volts
   c. 3.8 volts
   d. 5 volts

3. How long will it take for the capacitor in question 2 to discharge completely?

   a. 5 mS
   b. 10 mS
   c. 50 mS
   d. 250 mS

4. It takes a capacitor 80 microseconds to fully charge. The time constant is:

   a. 8 mS
   b. 16 mS
   c. 40 mS
   d. 80 mS

5. For given values of R and C, if the capacitance is doubled and the resistance is halved, the time constant will:

   a. remain the same
   b. double
   c. quadruple
   d. be reduced to half

EXPERIMENT 15 ➤ Testing Capacitors

OBJECTIVE

When you complete this experiment, you will be able to test for defective capacitors using a multimeter.

MATERIALS REQUIRED

- Digital multimeter
- Components
  one–100 μF electrolytic capacitor
  one–47 μF paper or plastic capacitor
  one–01 μF disc capacitor

INTRODUCTION

It is frequently necessary to test a capacitor when performing various troubleshooting, repair or design jobs. Special test instruments are available for this purpose. You may not have access to them, and usually, they are not necessary. You can use a multimeter, either analog or digital, to perform most basic capacitor tests. In this experiment we will show you how to use your digital multimeter for this purpose.

CAPACITOR FAILURE

There are three basic ways that a capacitor can fail. First, it can become *open*. That is, one or even both of the leads can break away from the plates. This circuit is as if there was absolutely no electrical connection.

Another way that a capacitor fails is to become *shorted*. In this type of failure, the plates touch or become shorted in some other way. A short is a very low resistance connection and the effect is as if the two capacitor leads were connected directly together.

A capacitor can also fail by developing *leakage*. Leakage is resistance that appears between the plates. The capacitor appears to have some value of resistance in parallel with it.

Shorts, opens, and leakage can be detected with a multimeter set for ohmmeter operation (multimeter set as ohmmeter = resistance detection).

TESTING THE CAPACITOR

To test a capacitor, connect its leads across the multimeter leads and measure the capacitor's resistance. A short will be indicated by a very low resistance value. An open circuit will be indicated by no measurement at all on the multimeter. Leakage will be indicated by a specific value of resistance. Also remember that when a digital multimeter "sees" an open circuit, it usually shows a one in the left-most digit position of the LCD display.

TO RE-CAP

To make resistance measurements, the multimeter must actually apply a voltage to the external component. A battery in the multimeter is used for this purpose. This voltage is applied to the external component (a resistor or a capacitor) through the ohmmeter circuitry. The multimeter, when used for resistance measurements, is referred to as an ohmmeter. They have a very high internal resistance. That value of resistance is determined by the range to which the multimeter is set. The higher the resistance range, the higher the internal resistance of the multimeter.

SUMMARY

It takes a finite amount of time for a capacitor to charge; so, when testing large values of capacitance you will note a varying reading on the multimeter. This will occur as the capacitor is charging to the internal voltage supplied by the multimeter. Normally this indication will appear to be a very low value of resistance. It will gradually increase until the capacitor is fully charged, at which time an open circuit will be indicated. You will demonstrate this phenomenon in the following procedure.

PROCEDURE

1. Set up your multimeter for DC resistance measurements. Set it to the 200 kilohm range.

100 µF CAPACITOR

2. Locate the 100 µF capacitor. Momentarily touch its leads together to remove any charge that may be on it.

3. Touch the probes of the multimeter to the leads of the 100 µF capacitor; the red lead to the plus terminal, and the black lead to the minus terminal. Note the effect that you see on the LCD display. Hold the probes on the capacitor leads and observe the display until an open circuit is indicated. (Remember: A one in the left-hand display.)

4. Considering the resistance changes you noted during the measurement in step 3, explain what is happening.

5. Next, discharge the capacitor by touching its leads together for several seconds. Then set the range switch to the 2 kilohm position.

6. Touch the probes to the capacitor terminals, black to minus and red to plus. Note the effect on the LCD display.

7. Explain the results you obtained in step 6 and compare it to the result you obtained in step 4.

.47 µF CAPACITOR

8. Locate the .47 µF capacitor. Touch its leads together momentarily to discharge it.

9. Set the multimeter to the 20 M range. Check the capacitor by touching the probes to the leads and note the effect on the LCD display.

10. Discharge the capacitor by touching its leads together for several seconds. Set the multimeter to the 2 M range. Then, again, test the capacitor by touching the probes to the capacitor leads. Make note of the effect on the LCD display.

.01 µF CAPACITOR

11. Locate the .01 µF capacitor. Touch its leads together momentarily to discharge it.

12. Set the multimeter to the 2 M position. Touch the multimeter probes to the capacitor leads and note the meter indication. *NOTE:* When making the connections of the probes to the capacitor leads, **do not** make physical contact with your fingers.

13. Now, discharge the capacitor by touching the leads together momentarily. This time, connect the multimeter probes to the capacitor leads, *but make the connections by holding them with your fingers.* Use the thumb and forefinger of each hand to hold one of the probes to the capacitor leads. Make note of the LCD indication.

14. Explain the results obtained in the previous two steps.

REVIEW QUESTIONS

1. When a multimeter is set as an ohmmeter what are you testing for?

    a. Voltage
    b. Current
    c. Resistance

2. When a multimeter is measuring an open circuit, the LCD should read:

    a. 0
    b. 1
    c. a very high value
    d. a very low value

3. When testing a capacitor with a multimeter, a reading of 275 kilohms is obtained. The capacitor:

   a. is good
   b. is open
   c. is shorted
   d. has leakage

4. A capacitor shows no charge indication on the multimeter. Which of the following indications is correct?

   a. The capacitor may have a very small value.
   b. A low resistance range is used.
   c. The capacitor may be open.
   d. All of the above.
   e. None of the above.

5. Touching the leads of a resistor, capacitor or the meter probes could cause a false measurement.

   a. True
   b. False

Section 2

AC
EXPERIMENTS

EXPERIMENT 16 ➤ Oscilloscope Familiarization

OBJECTIVES

When you complete this experiment, you will be able to use the oscilloscope controls to display a waveform and make DC and AC amplitude and frequency measurements.

MATERIALS REQUIRED

- Oscilloscope
- Multimeter
- Function generator
- DC power supply

INTRODUCTION

An oscilloscope is a relatively easy instrument to use, once you learn how. The major obstacle is learning and remembering the function of each of the various front panel controls. Oscilloscopes have a front panel full of knobs, dials, switches, pushbuttons, and connectors. For the uninitiated, it seems formidable. Learn what each control does and experience its effect on the display; you will then quickly understand its meaning and use. The best way to learn to use the oscilloscope is to get as much hands-on operating experience as possible.

THE OSCILLOSCOPE

The oscilloscope you are using is probably a dual-trace type (it can display two separate signals simultaneously). Therefore, it has two input cables and connectors. These are usually labeled as channels 1 and 2 or A and B. Each cable also has a name; there are two basic types, direct and attenuator.

OSCILLOSCOPE CABLES

The *direct type* is a coax cable with two leads, usually terminated in alligator clips for connecting to the circuit. This cable might use probe tips instead of two alligator clips. In any case, this arrangement connects the signal to be displayed directly to the oscilloscope through the coax cable.

The attenuator-type connector also uses a coax cable but generally uses a probe instead of alligator clips. The probe assembly contains a high-value series resistor, which forms a voltage divider with the input impedance of the oscilloscope. Thus this probe and cable attenuate (weaken) the signal by a factor of 10.

The benefit of such a cable is that it produces less capacitive loading of high frequency circuits, making it possible to view high frequency signals and complex waveforms. The trade-off is loss of signal amplitude, which can usually be corrected by increasing the oscilloscope gain. To get the correct amplitude measurement of a signal the scope setting is multiplied by 10. Such probes are called X10 or "times 10" probes.

AMPLITUDE MEASUREMENT

To make an amplitude measurement on an oscilloscope, the calibrated grid or graticule on the face of the CRT is used to determine the number of divisions between the maximum positive and maximum negative excursions of the signal (called a peak-to-peak measurement). Follow these steps:

Measurement Steps—Amplitude

1. Set the vertical gain control switch to display as large a signal as possible on the graticule.

2. Set the continuous vertical gain control knob to the CAL (calibrate) position.

3. Count the number of divisions and fractions thereof between the positive and negative peaks. Use the vertical position control to move the signal as needed. Note that most oscilloscopes have eight large vertical divisions divided into five smaller increments.

4. Multiply the number of divisions by the setting on the vertical gain switch. This is the peak-to-peak value.

5. If you are using a X10 probe, multiply your value in step 4 by 10. This is the corrected peak-to-peak voltage value.

Example: The vertical gain is set to 50 mV/div. This means that each large vertical increment represents 50 millivolts. Each of the five smaller divisions represents $50/5 = 10$ mV.

Assume your signal amplitude covers 6.3 divisions. The amplitude is $50 \times 6.3 = 315$ mV. If an X10 probe is used, the amplitude is $315 \times 10 = 3150$ mV or 3.15 volts.

FREQUENCY MEASUREMENT

To measure frequency (f) on the oscilloscope, first measure the period (t) of waveform. The period is the time for one cycle. The easiest way to do this is to count the number of horizontal divisions between two consecutive peaks of the signal. Follow these steps:

Measurement Steps—Frequency

1. Set the horizontal sweep switch to display one or two cycles of the signal.

2. Be sure the continuous horizontal frequency control is set to the CAL (calibrate) position.

3. Count the number of divisions between consecutive peaks. Use the horizontal position control to move the signal.

4. Multiply the number of divisions by the setting on the horizontal sweep control. This is the period (t).

5. To compute the frequency (f), find the reciprocal: $f = 1/t$.

Example: The horizontal sweep switch is set to 20 μS/division. Count 4.4 divisions between consecutive peaks. The period (t) is 4.4 x 20 = 88 μS. The frequency is:

$$f = 1/(88 \times 10^{-6}) = 11363.64 \text{ Hz or } 11.4 \text{ kHz}$$

PROCEDURE

1. Examine the oscilloscope probes to determine which kind you have. Record this:

    CH A _____

    CH B _____

2. Turn on the power to the oscilloscope with the front panel switch. Give the CRT a minute or so to warm up.

    a. While you are doing this, set the sweep Mode control switch to the Auto position.

    b. Set the Source switch to the CH 1 or CH A position.

    c. Set the Horizontal Position control to mid-range.

    d. A Vertical Position control is provided for both input channels; set them to the mid-range position as well.

    e. Set the Input switch on each channel to the GND position.

    f. As the oscilloscope warms up, you should see a bright horizontal line displayed across the screen. Turn the vertical position control to move the horizontal line to the center of the screen.

3. The trace on the screen should be bright and sharp. If it is not, correct this with the Focus and Intensity controls that are usually located on the front panel. Using the focus control, you should be able to make the line blurry and then bring it into sharp focus. Also vary the intensity control; this sets the brightness level of the line. However, do not make the line *too* bright or it will be too wide and reduce the accuracy of your measurements. *NOTE:* As a general rule, make the brightness as low as possible for comfortable viewing in normal ambient lighting.

4. Connect the probe tip for CH 1 to the small connector on the front panel labeled CAL. The oscilloscope contains a built-in multivibrator that runs at 1 kHz and puts out a square wave with a peak-to-peak amplitude of some stated voltage. This internally calibrated signal allows you to quickly check the oscilloscope frequency and amplitude measurements for correct calibrations.

$$\text{CAL voltage} \underline{\hspace{3cm}} V_{PP}$$

Set the front panel controls so that the variable horizontal and vertical controls are full clockwise (CW) to the CAL positions. Then set the horizontal sweep frequency with the TIME/DIV switch to the .1 mS position. Finally, set the vertical gain with the VOLTS/DIV switch to the 50 mV position.

5. Even though you have applied the calibrate signal to the vertical input of the oscilloscope, no signal is displayed. The reason is that you have previously set the input switch to the GND (ground) position. This simply grounds the input line and gives you the zero volt input *reference* position. You may now take the vertical position control and move it up and down to set it so that one of the horizontal lines on the graticule represents zero volt.

Set the input switch to the AC position. Immediately, you should see the 1 kHz square wave on the screen. Adjust the vertical and horizontal position control so that it can be seen clearly. *NOTE:* When you set the input switch to AC, you connected a capacitor in series with the input line. For that reason, any DC voltage on the input signal is blocked, and only the AC component of the signal will be displayed. That is what is occurring in this case. If you set the zero volt line to the center horizontal line, you will note that the square wave signal is switching above and below the zero line. In other words, the blocking capacitor inside the scope is eliminating the DC output of the multivibrator so you are displaying an AC version of the signal.

6. Next, use the variable vertical gain control to vary the amplitude of the signal. As you turn the control, note that you can change its amplitude over a wide range. This allows you to conveniently fit the signal onto the screen for observation. Remember, however, that in order to make accurate measurements, this variable control must be in the full clockwise or CAL position. Only then are the voltage-per-division designations on the vertical gain control correct.

AC Experiments

Rotate the variable horizontal sweep control. What are you doing now is changing the sweep speed of the sawtooth internally. Therefore, you can display more or fewer cycles of the waveform. Again, this control lets you conveniently adjust the number of cycles for display. For measuring the period or other *time elements* of the signal, however, the variable sweep control must be in the full clockwise or CAL position in order for the time per division switch settings to be correct.

7. Set the input switch to the DC position and note the effect on the waveform. You may have to adjust the vertical position and/or horizontal position controls to bring the waveform back into view. To temporarily locate and set the zero line, set the input switch back to the GND position. Then set the position control on one of the horizontal lines on the lower part of the screen. This is the zero volt reference line.

Now set the input switch back to the DC position. Note that the square wave occurs *above* the zero line. This means that the square wave is switching from approximately zero volt to the peak signal value. Note that when the waveform deflects upward from a base zero line, it represents a positive voltage. If the voltage deflects downward from the zero line, it is a negative voltage.

8. Measure the amplitude of the signal. Be sure the vertical variable gain control is full clockwise in the calibrate position. Count the number of vertical divisions between the bottom part of the square wave and the top part of the square wave. For example, if the CAL voltage is .25 volts or 250 mV_{pp}, you should count five divisions when the scope is set to the 50 mV position. Five positions of 50 millivolts each gives a peak-to-peak voltage of 25 millivolts. If you are using an x10 attenuator probe, set the vertical gain control to 5 mV per division, then multiply this value by 10 to get 250 mV.

Cal voltage = _____ V_{pp}

The internal calibrator circuit is not incredibly accurate, but the waveform displayed should be approximately equal to the value stated on the front panel.

9. Measure the frequency of the waveform. Most calibrators use a frequency of 1 kHz, but another value can also be used. Set the TIME/DIV switch to the 1 mS position. Check to see that the variable sweep control is in the CAL position. This means that each horizontal division on the screen represents 1 millisecond. You should be able to see that one cycle of the square wave takes up one millisecond on the screen. Remember that one cycle is made up of one positive-going and one negative-going pulse.

Set the TIME/DIV switch to the .1 mS position. Now each division represents .1 mS or 100 µS. Since the period of the 1 kHz signal is 1 millisecond, then one complete cycle of the signal should occupy the entire screen (10 horizontal divisions). Move the horizontal position control back and forth so that you can see that the positive edge of the pulse on the left hand side of the screen starts at the far left hand line and then the next positive-going pulse starts approximately at the far right hand vertical line. Repeat this move so that you can be more familiar with this. Again, the calibrator is not totally precise so the duration of one cycle may be slightly more or less than the full 10 horizontal divisions on the screen. What is the measured calibrator frequency?

CAL frequency = _____ Hz

10. While you are displaying this waveform, set the MODE switch to the NORM position. If the trace disappears, adjust the triggering level control until the signal appears again. You are now using the *triggered sweep feature* of the oscilloscope. You can adjust the trigger level or the point on the waveform where the signal starts the horizontal sweep. Since the input signal is a positive-going pulse, the triggering will occur on a positive voltage. Vary the trigger control in both clockwise and counterclockwise directions and note the effect on the waveform. Set it so the signal is displayed.

    Pull the trigger level knob out. This switch changes the triggering polarity. Now you will note that the waveform starts at the left hand side of the screen in the negative-going direction rather than in the positive-going direction as before. Later, when you display sine waves, you will again examine and become more familiar with this triggering function.

11. Connect the oscilloscope cable to a function generator output.

12. Set the function generator to supply a sine wave at 1 kHz. Turn the amplitude or output level control on the function generator to the full clockwise position.

    You should see a sine wave of approximately 1 kHz displayed on the oscilloscope screen. If the screen is blank, you might have the Mode switch in the NORM position and the trigger level is not correctly adjusted. Readjust the triggering knob until the waveform is displayed. Then adjust the vertical gain and the horizontal sweep switch positions so that you display several cycles of the sine wave on the screen. Play around with the controls until you get a satisfactory display.

13. You will now explore the frequency range of the function generator. Set the range switch on the function generator to the lowest position and rotate the frequency control to the full counterclockwise position. Set the scope Mode control knob to the AUTO position. What you will see is a horizontal line across the screen moving up and down at a slow rate. The slow rate is because the *sweep frequency* of your oscilloscope is too fast for you to display a full cycle of the sine wave being generated by the function generator at this low frequency. You can get an idea of the frequency by counting the number of times that the sine wave rises and falls. It should take approximately one second for the sine wave to move from its lowest to its highest position and then return.

While you are observing the sine wave, begin rotating the frequency knob in the clockwise direction. The speed of the up and down motion should begin to increase. At some point you should be able to switch the TIME/DIV switch to a higher position and you should observe a low frequency sine wave.

Switch the range switch on the function generator to the next higher position and note the effect on the screen. The frequency should immediately increase to a much higher value and you will see many more cycles displayed on the screen. Rotate the TIME/DIV switch to a higher position and note the sine wave being displayed. Vary the frequency control on the function generator to see how the frequency changes.

Continue this process by switching the function generator to the higher frequency positions and varying the frequency control over its full range. This, as you will observe, will continue to increase the frequency. As you increase the frequency, the sine waves will no longer be visible unless you spread them out by using the horizontal TIME/DIV switch. Each time you increase the frequency, you have to shorten the sweep rate in order to observe the waveform.

14. As a final observation of the frequency of the function generator, set the range switch to its highest position and rotate the frequency to the full clockwise position. What you will see is the highest frequency that the function generator can put out. Using the technique described earlier, set the time base switch to a convenient position. Then measure the period between adjacent positive or negative peaks. Estimate the time for the period, then calculate the frequency. What is the approximate highest frequency output from the function generator?

Maximum frequency _____ Hz

15. While you are observing the maximum output frequency from the function generator, you should also measure the amplitude of this signal.

    a. Be sure that the amplitude control is at its full clockwise position. This is the maximum output voltage that can be obtained from the function generator without a load.

    b. Set the variable gain control on the vertical input to the full clockwise or calibrate position.

    c. Set the VOLTS/DIV switch to the convenient position for measurement.

    d. Use the vertical position control to move the waveform up and down so that you can count the number of divisions between the negative peak and the positive peak.

    e. Count the number of divisions and multiply by the volts per division value. Then multiply again by a factor of 10 if you are using an attenuator probe.

    f. What is the maximum output that you can obtain from the function generator?

    Maximum voltage _____ volts (pp)

Finally, demonstrate how to reduce the output voltage of the waveform by rotating the function generator amplitude control in the counter clockwise direction. You should be able to reduce the output to a very low level, but output will not go all the way to zero and, at the lower amplitudes the waveform is somewhat distorted. In any case, you can vary the output waveform over a fairly wide range.

16. Most function generators also produce square and/or triangular waves. If you would like to observe the other waveforms produced by the function generator, you can do so by setting the front panel controls. Look at the triangular wave. Is it AC or DC? Look at the square wave. Is it AC or DC?

    Triangular wave _____

    Square wave _____

REVIEW QUESTIONS

1. A x10 scope probe:

   a. attenuates the input signal by a factor of 10
   b. amplifies the signal by a factor of 10

2. The distance between positive and negative peaks of a sine wave is 6.4 divisions. The vertical gain is set to 50 μV/division. A x10 probe is used. The peak-to-peak voltage value is:

   a. 3.2 μV
   b. 32 μV
   c. 320 μV
   d. 3.2 mV

3. The horizontal distance between adjacent peaks of a sine wave is 4.7 divisions. The sweep speed is 2 μS/division. The sine wave frequency is:

   a. 63.5 kHz
   b. 94 kHz
   c. 106.38 kHz
   d. 176.24 kHz

4. What waveform is not normally produced by a function generator?

   a. Sine
   b. Sawtooth
   c. Square
   d. Triangular

5. What control do you use to move the signal up and down on the scope screen?

   a. Horizontal gain
   b. Vertical gain
   c. Horizontal position
   d. Vertical position

EXPERIMENT 17 ➤ Sine Wave Measurements

OBJECTIVES

When you complete the experiment you will be able to measure sine wave voltages with a multimeter and oscilloscope and convert from rms to peak-to-peak and vice versa.

MATERIALS REQUIRED

- Multimeter (DMM)
- Oscilloscope
- Function generator
- DC power supply
- 2.7 kΩ resistor

INTRODUCTION

There are two common ways to measure sine wave voltages, with a multimeter and an oscilloscope. When a multimeter is used, the meter reads directly in volts as displayed on the scale by the pointer on an analog meter or as a decimal number on the LED or LCD readout of a digital meter. The value presented is the effective or root mean square (rms) value. It is also the more accurate reading.

The oscilloscope displays the sine wave on the screen. It is the easiest and most accurate way to measure the peak-to-peak value. Of the two devices, the meter value is the more accurate, as just mentioned. However, the oscilloscope lets you *see* the signal and any noise, distortion or interference that may accompany it.

EQUIPMENT LIMITATIONS

The multimeter has a restricted upper frequency limit. It varies with the meter, but is usually no more than several thousand Hz. The scope, of course, can measure voltages to the many MHz.

The multimeter also lets you measure current, whereas the scope does not. By inserting the meter in series with the circuit or component, you can get a reading of the rms current. The only way to measure current with a scope is indirectly by measuring the voltage across a resistor, converting from peak-to-peak to rms, then dividing by the resistor value.

CONVERSION FORMULAS

A common need, when making electronic tests and measurements, is converting from rms to peak-to-peak and vice versa. To convert from rms to peak-to-peak, use these formulas:

$$V_{PP} = 2.828\ V_{rms}$$
$$I_{PP} = 2.828\ I_{rms}$$

To convert from peak-to-peak to rms, use these formulas:

$$V_{rms} = .3535\ V_{PP}$$
$$I_{rms} = .3535\ I_{PP}$$

Example. To convert a reading of 6.3 V_{PP} to rms:

$$V_{rms} = .3535(6.3) = 2.23\ V$$

Example. To convert a current reading of 7 mA to a peak-to-peak value:

$$I_{PP} = 2.828(7) = 19.8\ mA$$

Oscilloscopes can also measure DC. A vertical shift in a horizontal line on the screen represents a DC input. To measure DC, set the vertical position of the horizontal line on a graticule line with zero input. Apply the DC input, then measure the vertical distance shift in divisions and convert to voltage.

SUMMARY

You will demonstrate the measurement of sine wave voltages and currents and the conversion between units in this procedure.

PROCEDURE

1. Turn the oscilloscope on and display a horizontal trace.

2. Turn on the signal generator, select sine wave output, and set the dial for 1 kHz. Connect the generator output to the scope. Display the signal. Adjust the scope for a stable display. Adjust the generator output for a signal amplitude of 4 V_{PP}.

3. Calculate the effective (rms) value of this sine wave. Measure the sine wave with the DMM. Compare your calculated and measured values.

V_{rms} (calculated) _____ volts

V_{rms} (measured) _____ volts

4. Measure the period of the sine wave on the scope.

$$T = \underline{\hspace{3cm}} \text{ sec}$$

5. Calculate the frequency of the sine wave from the period you measured. Compare your measured and calculated values and the setting of the generator dial.

$$f = \underline{\hspace{3cm}} \text{ Hz}$$

6. Repeat steps 2–5 with a 500 mV sine wave at 60 Hz and a 15 kHz, 3 V_{pp} square wave. What meaning does rms voltage have with regard to the sine wave?

7. Connect the generator output to the 2.7 kilohm resistor. Adjust the generator to supply 9 V_{pp} at 120 Hz to the resistor. Monitor the voltage with the scope.

8. Calculate the current in the resistor using Ohm's law.

$$I = \underline{\hspace{3cm}} \text{ mA}$$

9. Measure the current in the resistor using the DMM. Compare your measured and calculated values.

$$I = \underline{\hspace{3cm}} \text{ mA}$$

10. Disconnect the generator and resistor. Turn on one of the lab's DC power supplies. Adjust it for an output of +6 volts. Measure this output on the scope and the DMM. Repeat for a DC voltage of –12 volts.

11. Connect the signal generator output in series with the DC power supply and display the resulting signal. Set the DC power supply for +5 volts and adjust the signal generator for 400 Hz and 2 V_{pp}. Draw a diagram of the composite signal.

12. List as many possible sources of error that may account for the differences between the calculated and measured values in the previous steps.

REVIEW QUESTIONS

1. What is 85 mV peak-to-peak in rms?

   a. 6 mV
   b. 30 mV
   c. 170 mV
   d. 240 mV

2. What is 16 µA rms in peak-to-peak?

   a. 5.7
   b. 11.3
   c. 7.07
   d. 14.14

3. A multimeter gives reading in:

   a. peak
   b. peak-to-peak
   c. rms
   d. average

4. An oscilloscope can measure DC.

   a. True
   b. False

5. Which gives more accurate measurements?

   a. Oscilloscope
   b. Multimeter

EXPERIMENT 18 ➤ Inductors and AC

OBJECTIVE

When you complete this experiment, you will be able to explain the effect of inductance in an AC circuit and calculate the values of inductance and reactance from measurements.

MATERIALS REQUIRED

- Oscilloscope
- Digital multimeter
- 100 mH inductor
- Function/signal generator

INTRODUCTION

When an inductor is connected into an AC circuit, the continuous *voltage* variations produce *current* variations that, in turn, generate a rising and falling magnetic field. This magnetic field induces a voltage back into the inductor, which opposes the current variations. The result is a continuous opposition to current flow. This opposition is known as inductive reactance (X_L).

REACTANCE FORMULA

The inductive reactance of a coil or choke is dependent upon the frequency of the applied AC (f) and the value of inductance (L) in henries. The inductive reactance expressed in ohms is calculated with the simple formula:

$$X_L = 2\pi f L$$

The reactance is directly proportional to the frequency and the inductance. If the inductive reactance is known, either the frequency or the inductance itself may be calculated by simply rearranging the basic formula as shown:

$$L = X_L/2\pi f \qquad f = X_L/2\pi L$$

IMPEDANCE FORMULA

Remember, there are no pure inductors because indicators **must** be made with wire that has resistance. The total opposition offered by an inductor to AC is, therefore, a combination of opposition offered by the inductive reactance and the resistance. This combined opposition is known as impedance. The impedance is calculated with the formula:

$$Z = \sqrt{(R)^2 + (X_L)^2}$$

Remember that the inductance causes the current to lag the voltage. For this reason, the voltages across the inductor and resistor are 90 degrees out of phase with one another. This prevents us from simply adding together the inductive reactance and the resistance to get the impedance.

If the impedance is known but either the reactance or resistance is not, the previous formula can be rearranged to compute them.

$$X_L = \sqrt{(Z)^2 - (R)^2} \qquad\qquad R = \sqrt{(Z)^2 - (X_L)^2}$$

If the impedance of an inductive circuit is known, you can calculate the current in the circuit if you know the applied voltage. This is done by using Ohm's law.

$$I = V/Z$$

Of course, this formula can also be rearranged to calculate for the other two variables if the problem calls for it.

$$Z = V/I \qquad\qquad V = IZ$$

SUMMARY

In this experiment you will demonstrate the effect of inductance in an AC circuit.

PROCEDURE

1. Measure the resistance of the inductor winding with the multimeter.

    DC resistance = _____ ohms

2. Connect the 100 mH inductor to a signal generator supplying 4 V_{pp} at 400 Hz.

3. Now measure the actual value of primary current. Remember that an ammeter must be inserted in *series* with the circuit to make the measurement. Connect the multimeter to measure AC current. Be sure the generator continues to supply 4 V_{pp}.

    I_S = _____ mA

4. Using the information you have collected in the previous steps and the formulas reviewed in the Introduction, calculate the total circuit impedance.

    Z = _____ ohms

5. Using the information calculated in the previous steps and the formulas described in the Introduction, calculate the inductance (*L*) of the coil.

    L = _____ H

REVIEW QUESTIONS

1. Increasing the frequency of the AC applied to an inductor causes the reactance to:

   a. increase
   b. decrease
   c. remain the same

2. Decreasing the value of inductance in a circuit causes the reactance to:

   a. increase
   b. decrease
   c. remain the same

3. Decreasing the resistance of an inductor causes its impedance to:

   a. increase
   b. decrease
   c. remain the same

4. The unit for expressing inductive reactance is:

   a. henries
   b. farads
   c. watts
   d. ohms

5. An inductor has a resistance of 120 ohms. When 24 volts AC at 60 Hz is applied, a current of 111 mA flows. The inductance value is about:

   a. .12 H
   b. .35 H
   c. .48 H
   d. 1.2 H

EXPERIMENT 19 ➤ Transformer Operation

OBJECTIVE

When you complete this experiment, you will be able to explain the operation of a transformer in an AC circuit and calculate voltage step-up and step-down ratios.

MATERIALS REQUIRED

- Dual trace oscilloscope
- Digital multimeter
- Power transformer
- Function/signal generator
- Components
  100 ohm resistor
  1 kΩ resistor

INTRODUCTION

A transformer is an electronic component with one or more windings of wire, usually on an iron core or frame. The purpose of the transformer is to transfer electrical energy from one circuit to another by way of a magnetic field. Transformers are used for voltage step-up and step-down, and impedance matching.

TRANSFORMER SCHEMATIC

Figure 19–1 shows a typical schematic diagram of a transformer. When AC voltage is applied to the left hand winding (the primary), current flows. The current produces a varying magnetic field that cuts the turns of the right hand winding (the secondary). Though there is no physical contact between the two windings, the magnetic field induces a voltage into the secondary winding. That voltage can then be used to power another circuit.

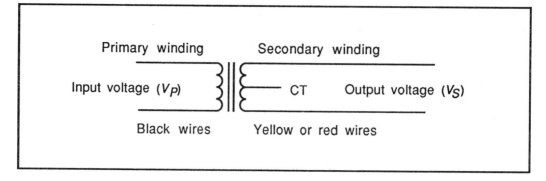

Figure 19–1

The amount of voltage induced into the secondary winding is a result of the number of the turns in each winding. The ratio of the number of turns in the secondary winding (N_S) to the number of turns in the primary winding (N_p) is known as the *turns ratio* and is expressed mathematically as:

$$\text{Turns Ratio} = N = N_S/N_p$$

DETERMINING VOLTAGE

You can determine the amount of voltage produced across the secondary winding (V_S) by simply multiplying the voltage applied to the primary (V_p) by the turns ratio. This formula is:

$$V_S = V_P(N_S/N_p)$$

If the turns ratio is greater than 1, the secondary voltage will be higher than the primary voltage: a step-up transformer. When the turns ratio is less than 1, the secondary voltage will be less than the primary voltage: a step-down transformer.

The turns ratio and the voltage ratio are related as follows:

$$N = N_S/N_p = V_S/V_P$$

DETERMINING PRIMARY AND SECONDARY CURRENTS

Since the power output of a transformer is *very nearly equal* to the power input, the turns ratio can also be used to determine the primary and secondary currents (I_p and I_S). It is a reverse relationship as the following expression shows.

$$I_P/I_S = N_S/N_p$$

The connections of a transformer winding can be such that the output is in phase with the input or 180 degrees out of phase with it. The phase can be changed by simply reversing the connections to *one* winding. If the transformer is wired to produce a 180-degree phase shift, the secondary voltage is said to be *inverted*.

Some transformers have taps on the winding to provide multiple output voltages. A common connection is the center tap (CT) on the secondary winding, which provides two voltages equal to one-half the total secondary winding voltage. (See Figure 19–1.)

SUMMARY

In this experiment, you will demonstrate transformer action. You will also learn to measure transformer voltages and compute the turns ratio.

PROCEDURE

1. Connect the primary winding (black wires) of the transformer to the signal generator output. Apply a sine wave voltage of 100 Hz. Set the voltage on the primary to 10 V_{PP}. Monitor the signal on the oscilloscope.

2. Note the three other wires coming out of the transformer. Two of them are the same color, usually yellow or red. These are the connections to the secondary winding. The third wire is a different color, usually blue, and is the center tap of the winding. *NOTE:* The ends of the wires are probably bare, so be careful that they do not touch one another and cause a short circuit. If the secondary winding wires are not bare at the ends, strip about ½" of insulation from the end of each.

3. Turn on the signal generator. Using your multimeter, measure the AC voltage appearing across the two yellow or red secondary wires. Do *not* touch the wires while making this connection. Record this voltage:

   Secondary voltage (V_S) = _____ volts

4. While making your measurements, measure the voltage between the blue lead and each of the yellow leads. Record your value:

   Voltage between blue lead and first yellow lead = _____ volts

   Voltage between blue lead and second yellow lead = _____ volts

5. Using the data you have collected in steps 1 and 3, calculate the turns ratio of this transformer as well as the primary and secondary currents. Assume a 100 ohm secondary load.

   Turns ratio = _____

   I_P = _____

   I_S = _____

   Is this a step-up or step-down transformer? _____

6. Connect a 100-ohm resistor across the secondary wires. Again measure the secondary voltage.

   V_S = _____ volts

7. Connect the multimeter in series with the secondary winding. Measure the current.

   I_S = _____ mA

8. Compute the primary current.

   I_P = _____

9. Measure the primary current.

   I_P = _____ mA

10. Display the primary and secondary voltages on a dual-trace oscilloscope. What is the phase relationship between the primary and secondary voltages?

11. Reverse the secondary winding connections. Now what is the phase relationship between the primary and secondary voltages?

12. Disconnect the 100-ohm resistor. Reverse the primary and secondary windings. Use the yellow or red wires as the primary and connect them to the signal generator. Connect a 1 kilohm resistor across the secondary winding (black wires).

13. Set the signal generator to supply 12 volts peak-to-peak to the primary. Measure the secondary voltage.

$$V_S = \text{_____} \text{ volts}$$

Is this a step-up or step-down transformer?

14. Calculate the turns ratio plus the primary and secondary currents.

$$N = \text{_____}$$
$$I_P = \text{_____}$$
$$I_S = \text{_____}$$

15. Insert the multimeter in series with the 1 k load. Measure the secondary current.

$$I_S = \text{_____} \text{ mA}$$

16. Measure the primary current.

$$I_P = \text{_____} \text{ mA}$$

REVIEW QUESTIONS

1. A transformer has 1600 turns on the secondary and 500 turns on the primary. What kind of transformer is this?

   a. Step-up
   b. Step-down

2. If 120 volts is applied to the *primary* of the transformer described in step 6 in the procedure, what is the secondary voltage?

   a. 37.5 volts
   b. 120 volts
   c. 384 volts
   d. 462 volts

3. In the experiment, if the 120 volts was applied to the *secondary* winding in step 6, what voltage would you measure across the primary winding?

   a. 14 volts
   b. 120 volts
   c. 134 volts
   d. 1028 volts

4. An AC voltage of 240 volts is applied to a transformer primary. The secondary voltage is 48 volts. The turns ratio is:

   a. .12
   b. .2
   c. 1.8
   d. 5

5. If the secondary of the transformer in question 4 is center tapped, what is the voltage across one-half of the winding?

   a. 24 volts
   b. 48 volts
   c. 240 volts
   d. 600 volts

EXPERIMENT 20 ➤ Capacitors and AC

OBJECTIVE

When you complete this experiment, you will be able to calculate and measure the currents and voltages in series and parallel capacitive circuits.

MATERIALS REQUIRED

- Oscilloscope
- Digital multimeter
- Breadboarding socket
- DC power supply
- Function generator
- Components
  one–.01 μF capacitor
  one–10 kΩ resistor

INTRODUCTION

When a capacitor is used in an AC circuit, it exhibits a form of opposition known as capacitive reactance. Capacitive reactance, like resistance, opposes current flow, but only in an AC circuit. The reactance is measured in ohms and is a function of both the frequency of the AC and the value of the capacitor. The reactance is inversely proportional to the frequency (f) and the capacitance (C). It can be computed with the formula:

$$X_C = 1/2 \, \pi f C$$

Usually capacitors are combined with resistors and other components in various series and parallel configurations to make filters, phase shifters, coupling networks and other circuits. One of the most common configurations is a series resistor capacitor circuit, Figure 20–1.

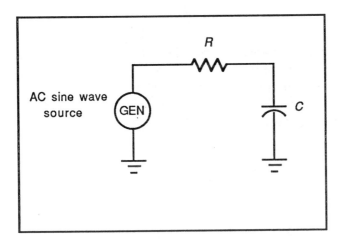

Figure 20–1

A source of a sine wave voltage (V_S) is applied to the resistor and capacitor connected in series. The total opposition to current flow in this circuit is a combination of both the resistance and the reactance. Resistors and capacitors operate in different ways, and because the capacitor produces a 90-degree phase shift in the circuit, the values of resistance and inductive reactance *cannot* be added directly to compute the total opposition to current flow called the impedance (Z). Instead, the formula given is used to determine the impedance of the circuit.

$$Z = \sqrt{(R)^2 + (X_C)^2}$$

THE PYTHAGOREAN THEOREM AND IMPEDANCE

This is the familiar Pythagorean theorem used to solve right triangles. The resistance, capacitive reactance, and impedance can all be represented by sides of a right triangle as shown in Figure 20–2A.

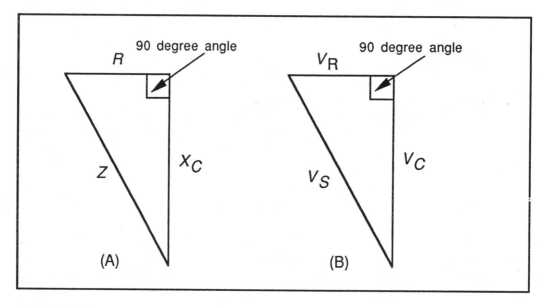

Figure 20–2

In a series circuit, the same current (I) flows through all of the components. This means that the capacitor current is the same as the resistive current and the same as the total current drawn from the voltage source. Since current is common to all components, we can use Ohm's law and multiply the current by the resistance, the capacitive reactance, and the impedance to compute the circuit voltages.

$$
\begin{aligned}
IR &= V_R \\
IX_C &= V_C \\
IZ &= V_S
\end{aligned}
$$

We can, therefore, redraw the triangle using the voltages we have derived in this way, Figure 20–2B. The triangle now represents the voltage across the resistance (V_R), the voltage across the capacitor (V_C), and the supply voltage (V_S). Kirchhoff's law says that the sum of the voltage drops around a series circuit equals the source voltage. This means that if we add the resistor and capacitor voltages, we *should* get the supply voltage. But as you can see in Figure 20–2B, the voltages are *out of phase with one another*. For this reason, the voltages cannot be directly added, and we must use the Pythagorean theorem to solve the right triangle. As a result, substitute the values from Figure 20–2B to the theorem format and compute the source voltage as shown:

$$V_S = \sqrt{(V_R)^2 + (V_C)^2}$$

To reiterate: To find the source voltage, simply measure the voltage across the resistor and capacitor, square each value, and add them together. Then, by taking the square root of that sum, the supply voltage is computed.

Remember, if you know the supply voltage and one of the other voltages, you can calculate the unknown voltage by simply rearranging the formula just given. Two additional versions of this formula then are:

$$V_R = \sqrt{(V_S)^2 - (V_C)^2} \qquad\qquad V_C = \sqrt{(V_S)^2 - (V_R)^2}$$

SUMMARY

In this experiment, you are going to demonstrate the fact that capacitors *do* represent an opposition to AC. You will then build a series RC circuit like the one just described and calculate then measure all the currents and voltages to verify this concept.

PROCEDURE 1: MEASURING PHASE SHIFT

To complete this experiment, you will need to measure the phase shift between two sine waves. To do this, display the two signals on a dual-trace oscilloscope. One signal, the upper trace, is used as a reference and connected to channel 1 or A. The other signal is connected to channel 2 or B. Then follow these steps.

1. Set the horizontal sweep speed to display one cycle of the sine waves. Set the continuous sweep to the CAL position.

2. Measure the period (t) of the sine waves as described in Experiment 16.

3. Measure the number of divisions between two adjacent or consecutive positive peaks of the sine waves.

4. Compute the time shift (t_1) by multiplying the number of divisions by the horizontal sweep setting.

AC Experiments **103**

5. Compute the phase shift with this formula:

$$\theta = 360\, t_1/t \text{ degrees}$$

Example: The period of the sine waves is 250 μS. The space between two adjacent positive peaks of the two signals is 2.6 divisions. The sweep speed is 10 μ/div. The time shift is:

$$t_1 = 2.6 \times 10 = 26\ \mu S$$

The phase shift is:

$$\theta = 360(26)/250 = 37.44^{\circ}$$

PROCEDURE 2: RC CIRCUIT

1. Connect the series RC circuit shown in Figure 20–3.

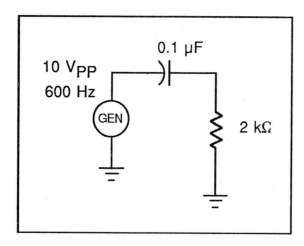

Figure 20–3

2. Adjust the generator frequency to 600 Hz. Set the voltage across the circuit to 10 volts peak-to-peak.

3. Make the following measurements with both the oscilloscope and the multimeter:

Oscilloscope		Multimeter	
$V_R =$ _____ volts		$V_R =$ _____ volts	
$V_C =$ _____ volts		$V_C =$ _____ volts	

Explain why they are different but equivalent. Draw the voltage triangles.

4. Make the following calculations for the circuit in Figure 20–3.

$$I = \underline{\hspace{3cm}} \text{ mA}$$

$$Z = \underline{\hspace{3cm}} \text{ ohms}$$

5. Measure the phase shift between the input voltage and output voltage.

$$\theta = \underline{\hspace{3cm}} \text{ degrees}$$

Does the output lead or lag the input? Why?

6. Change the input frequency to 1000 Hz. Be sure the generator voltage is still 10 volts peak-to-peak. Repeat steps 3, 4, and 5. State how the impedance and current vary with frequency by comparing your values in step 4.

7. Reverse the positions of the resistor and capacitor. Repeat step 5. Does the output lead or lag the input?

$$\theta = \underline{\hspace{3cm}} \text{ degrees}$$

8. Find the frequency at which $R = X_C$ in this circuit. Calculate the frequency first. Then, using the oscilloscope and audio generator, make measurements to verify your calculations.

$$f = \underline{\hspace{3cm}} \text{ Hz}$$

Explain what procedure you used and why.

9. Connect the parallel RC circuit shown in Figure 20–4. Calculate its total resistance (R_T), total capacitance (C_T) and impedance. Draw the current triangle.

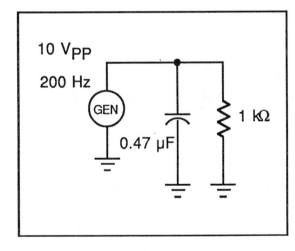

Figure 20–4

$$R_T = \underline{\hspace{3cm}} \text{ ohms}$$

$$C_T = \underline{\hspace{3cm}} \text{ } \mu\text{F}$$

$$Z = \underline{\hspace{3cm}} \text{ ohms}$$

10. Apply a voltage of 10 volts peak-to-peak at 200 Hz to the circuit. Measure the total circuit current using the multimeter. Calculate the impedance.

$$Z = \underline{\hspace{5cm}} \text{ ohms}$$

11. What is the phase shift between total current and applied voltage?

$$\theta = \underline{\hspace{4cm}}.$$

12. In all steps above, explain the differences between the measured and calculated values.

REVIEW QUESTIONS

1. Increasing the frequency applied to a series RC circuit will cause the voltage across the capacitor to:

   a. increase
   b. decrease
   c. remain the same
   d. drop to zero

2. Decreasing the capacitance in a series RC circuit will cause the circuit current to:

   a. increase
   b. decrease
   c. remain the same
   d. drop to zero

3. The voltage across the resistor in a series RC circuit is 3 volts. The voltage across the capacitor is 4 volts. The supply voltage is:

   a. 1 volt
   b. 3.5 volts
   c. 5 volts
   d. 7 volts

4. In a series RC circuit, the supply voltage is 6 volts. The circuit current is:

   a. .2 ohms
   b. 2 ohms
   c. 20 ohms
   d. 200 ohms

5. In a series RC circuit, the voltages across the components are: $V_R = 5$ volts and $V_C = 4$ volts. The resistor value is 1.5 kilohms. The frequency is 2 kHz. What is the capacitor value?

   a. .018 mF
   b. .047 mF
   c. .066 mF
   d. .075 mF

EXPERIMENT 21 ➤ LCR Circuits

OBJECTIVE

When you complete this experiment, you will be able to calculate and measure all of the currents, voltages, and impedances in a series LCR circuit.

MATERIALS REQUIRED:

- Oscilloscope
- Digital multimeter
- Breadboarding socket
- Function generator
- DC power supply
- Components
  one–100 mH inductor
  one–.1 µF capacitor
  one–470 ohm resistor

INTRODUCTION

An LCR circuit (also called an RLC circuit) consists of inductance, capacitance, and resistance. Whenever coils and capacitors are combined in an AC circuit, their reactances will cancel one another. **Remember:** an inductor causes the current to *lag* the applied voltage by 90 degrees; a capacitor causes the current to *lead* the voltage by 90 degrees.

As a result, the inductor cancels the capacitor because their actions are *opposite* one another. Also, in a series circuit containing inductance and capacitance, the component with the larger reactance will cancel the smaller reactance.

Example: in the circuit of Figure 21–1 with 100 ohms of inductive reactance and 75 ohms of capacitive reactance, the capacitive reactance will be cancelled completely, while the circuit will *appear* to have total inductive reactance of $100 - 75 = 25$ ohms. It is this combined total effective reactance that is used in computing the impedance of the circuit. The circuit appears inductive since X_L is greater than X_C.

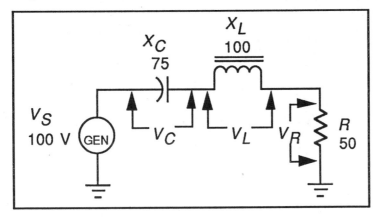

Figure 21–1

DETERMINING IMPEDANCE

The impedance of a series LCR circuit is determined with this formula:

$$Z = \sqrt{(R)^2 + (X_L - X_C)^2}$$
$$Z = \sqrt{(50)^2 + (25)^2}$$
$$Z = \sqrt{2500 + 625}$$
$$Z = \sqrt{3125}$$
$$Z = 55.9 \text{ ohms}$$

Once you know the total circuit impedance, you can, of course, find the circuit current with Ohm's law, assuming the source voltage (V_S) is known. This is done with the following expression, and substituting the figures just shown:

$$I = V_S/Z$$
$$I = 100/55.9 = 1.79 \text{ A}$$

Now, knowing that the current is the same in each component, you can determine the voltage drops across *each* of the components. Again this is done with Ohm's law and the formulas given:

$$V_R = IR = 1.79(50) = 89.5 \text{ volts}$$
$$V_C = IX_L = 1.79(100) = 179 \text{ volts}$$
$$V_L = IX_C = 1.79(75) = 134.25 \text{ volts}$$

As in any series circuit, the voltages distribute themselves in proportion to the values of the resistance and reactances: the larger voltages appear across the larger reactances. Just keep in mind that because of the phase shift produced by the circuit, you cannot simply add the component voltages directly to get the total source voltage. Phasor additions are required. Figure 21–2 shows how this is done using the previous example.

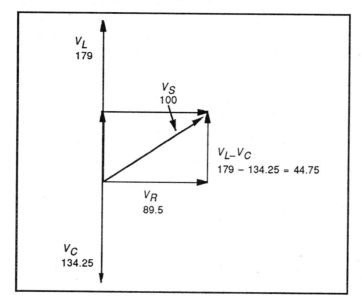

Figure 21–2

SUMMARY

In this experiment, you are going to build a series LCR circuit and make all of the calculations necessary to define the circuit. Then you will make measurements to verify your calculations.

PROCEDURE

1. Measure the resistance of the 100 mH inductor with the multimeter.

$$R_L = \text{_____} \text{ ohms}$$

2. Connect the circuit shown in Figure 21–3. Set the generator voltage to 4 volts peak-to-peak at 1 kHz.

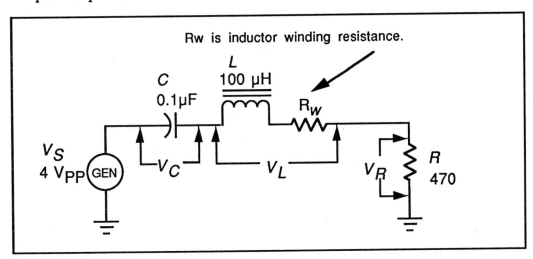

Figure 21–3

3. Measure V_R, V_L, V_C and θ and record them in the following table. Remember that 0 means the phase of the current or V_R to the applied voltage V_S.

4. Using the data in the table, calculate I and Z and record them in the table. Determine the STATUS of the circuit (either inductive or capacitive) and note it in the table.

Frequency	V_R	V_C	V_L	I	Z	θ	STATUS	P
1 kHz								
2 kHz								

5. Increase the generator frequency to 2 kHz. Keep the generator voltage at 4 V_{PP}.

6. Repeat steps 3 and 4 at the higher frequency. Record your data.

7. Draw the equivalent circuits at 1 kHz and 2 kHz and show the equivalent reactive component values in μF or mH as needed.

8. Calculate the real power (*P*) dissipated by the circuit at each frequency and record it in the table. Name the components that dissipate power and explain.

REVIEW QUESTIONS

1. An LCR circuit has the following values: X_L = 30 Ω, X_C = 42 Ω, R = 15 Ω. The circuit is:

   a. inductive, X_L = 12 Ω
   b. inductive, X_L = 72 Ω
   c. capacitive, X_L = 72 Ω
   d. capacitive, X_L = 12 Ω

2. In the circuit described in question 1, the smallest voltage drop will appear across the:

   a. resistor
   b. inductor
   c. capacitor

3. What is the total impedance of the circuit described in question 1?

   a. 15 ohms
   b. 19.2 ohms
   c. 72 ohms
   d. 87.5 ohms

4. A series LCR circuit will appear inductive if:

   a. $X_C > X_L$
   b. $X_C > V_L$
   c. $V_L > V_C$
   d. $X_L < X_C$

5. A .02 μF capacitor and a .047 μF capacitor are connected in parallel. The total equivalent capacitance is:

   a. .0094 μF
   b. .014 μF
   c. .0335 μF
   d. .067 μF

EXPERIMENT 22 ➤ Resonance

OBJECTIVE

When you complete this experiment, you will be able to calculate the resonant frequency of an LCR circuit and make measurements in the circuit to determine when the condition of resonance exists.

MATERIALS REQUIRED

- Oscilloscope
- Digital multimeter
- Breadboarding socket
- Function generator
- Components
  one–10 mH inductor
  one–.22 µF capacitor
  one–.47 µF capacitor
  one–100 ohm resistor

INTRODUCTION

Resonance is a condition in an LCR circuit where the inductive and capacitive reactances are equal. Since they are equal, they cancel one another completely. At resonance, many special effects occur; for example, because the reactive effects cancel one another at resonance, the circuit *appears* totally resistive.

You will encounter resonant circuits in almost every type of electronic equipment. They are widely used to perform a variety of tuning and filtering jobs in electronic equipment. In this experiment, you are going to demonstrate the effect of resonance with both series and parallel resonant circuits.

SERIES RESONANT CIRCUITS

A series resonance circuit is shown in Figure 22–1. Remember, when resonance occurs, the inductive and capacitive reactances cancel one another, leaving only the circuit resistance to impede current flow. In this circuit, the total impedance is simply the value of R plus the DC resistance of the coil. The main characteristic of a series resonant circuit is that its impedance is *minimum* at resonance. Tuning the frequency above or below the resonant point causes the impedance to rise.

AC Experiments   **111**

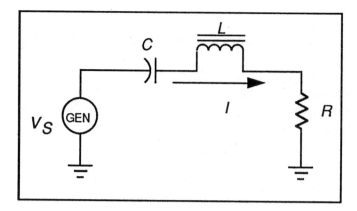

Figure 22-1

Because the impedance is minimum at resonance in a series resonant circuit, the current in the circuit will rise to a peak. This high value of current, when multiplied by the inductive and capacitive reactances produces very high voltage drops across these components. In fact, the voltage drops across the coil and capacitor at resonance are often *far greater* than the supply voltage. These unusually high voltages are referred to as resonant step-up voltages or resonant voltage rises.

PARALLEL RESONANT CIRCUITS

A parallel resonant circuit is shown in Figure 22-2. The coil and capacitor are connected across one another and the combination is sometimes connected in series with a resistor. Since at resonance the inductive and capacitive reactances cancel, the result is that the circuit appears to be a very *high* resistance value. The impedance of the parallel LC combination will rise to many thousands of ohms at resonance. At frequencies below and above resonance, the impedance decreases.

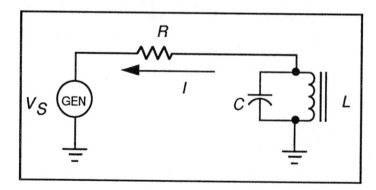

Figure 22-2

If you measure the line current in the resistor that is in series with the parallel resonance circuit, you will find that the current will reach a minimum at the resonant point. This is because at resonance the impedance is maximum and, therefore, it will produce the lowest value of circuit current. On either side of the resonant frequency, the impedance will decrease and the line current will increase.

The impedance of a parallel resonant circuit is calculated by using the formula:

$$Z = L/CR$$

Here, R is the resistance of the inductor L. For example, if $L = 2$ mH, $C = .05$ μF, and $R = 5$ Ω, then Z is:

$$Z = 2 \times 10^{-3}/(.05 \times 10^{-6})(5)$$

$$Z = 8000 \text{ ohms}$$

You can also use the formula:

$$Z = R_W(Q^2 + 1)$$

where R_W is the winding resistance of the coil and $Q = X_L/R_W$.

SUMMARY

As previously stated, in this experiment you will build both series and parallel resonant circuits and demonstrate some of these effects. You will also practice calculating the resonant frequency (f_r) given the inductor and capacitor values. This is done with the formula:

$$f_r = 1/2\pi \, (\sqrt{LC})$$

PROCEDURE

1. Refer to Figure 22–3. Calculate the resonant frequency given the values shown.

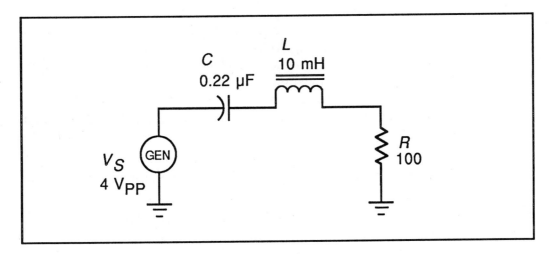

Figure 22–3

$$f_r = \underline{\hspace{4cm}} \text{ Hz}$$

2. Before building the circuit, measure the resistance of the inductor. This will affect the total circuit impedance.

Resistance of inductor = _____ ohms

NOTE: Steps 3–11 are to be recorded in Figure 22–4 as directed.

3. Calculate the total circuit impedance at resonance. Record your value:

	$Z\ (\Omega)$	$I\ (mA)$	$X_L\ (\Omega)$	$X_C\ (\Omega)$	V_L	V_C	V_R
CALCULATED							
MEASURED							

Figure 22–4

4. Next, compute the total circuit current. Record it:

5. Knowing the frequency of operation, determine the values of inductive and capacitive reactance. Using the resonant frequency you computed in step 1, calculate the inductive and capacitive reactances. Record your values:

6. Now calculate the voltage drops across each of the components in the circuit from the figures in step 5. Record your values:

7. Construct the circuit shown in Figure 22–3. Adjust the amplitude control on the function generator for a value of 4 volts peak-to-peak.

8. Monitor the voltage across the 100-ohm resistor with the oscilloscope. While monitoring the voltage, adjust the frequency control on the function generator for a maximum voltage reading. Make your adjustments slowly and allow the reading on the multimeter to settle down before making each new adjustment. NOTE: Tuning for the maximum value is slow and tedious, but take your time so that you will produce more accurate results. Keep tuning until this maximum voltage point is found. At this time the function generator is set to the resonant frequency of the circuit. Explain why this procedure is used to find f_r.

9. Go back and double check to see that the function generator output is 4 V_{PP}. Readjust the output to this value and repeat step 8 if necessary.

10. Once the circuit is adjusted to resonance, measure the voltage drops across each of the components. Record your values:

11. Break the circuit at the point where the .22 μF capacitor connects to the 100 ohm resistor as you did in the previous experiment. This will allow you to insert a multimeter to measure the circuit current. Set up your multimeter to measure AC current. Set the scale to the 2 mA range. Measure the circuit current and record your value:

12. Now compare your calculated and measured values. They should be the same or at least very close. Explain any differences.

13. While measuring the current in the series resonant circuit, vary the function generator output with the frequency control. Turn the knob slowly counterclockwise to reduce the frequency and note the effect on the current. Tuning the frequency slowly is so that you can better observe the effect on the multimeter reading, and because it takes several seconds for the reading to settle down after a change is made.

   Next, rotate the frequency control slowly in the clockwise direction, increasing the frequency, and again note the effect. When tuning the frequency above and below the resonant point, you should find a wide current variation. While observing this variation, determine just what effect the frequency has on the current.

14. Reconnect the 100-ohm resistor and the .22 μF capacitor.

15. Connect the probes of the oscilloscope across the capacitor and inductor simultaneously. Vary the frequency control on the function generator for a minimum voltage level. When the lowest possible voltage is reached, the circuit is adjusted to resonance. Make note of the position of the pointer on the function generator frequency control. Explain what you did here.

16. Remove the .22 μF capacitor from the breadboarding socket, and in its place, install the .47 μF capacitor. Calculate the resonant frequency of this new combination.

$$f_r = \rule{3cm}{0.4pt} \text{ Hz}$$

   With the capacitance in the circuit increased to .47 μF, the resonant frequency has:

   _____ Increased   _____ Decreased

17. Again connect the oscilloscope probes across the capacitor and inductor combination. Adjust the frequency control of the function generator and tune for minimum voltage. Once the minimum voltage point has been reached, note the direction in which you rotated the function generator control. Is the frequency higher or lower than previously?

   _____ Higher   _____ Lower

   Does this correspond to the results you predicted in step 16?

18. Construct the parallel resonant circuit shown in Figure 22–5. Note that the two capacitors are connected in series, and this combination is connected across the inductor. This forms the parallel resonant circuit where the two series capacitors have a single equivalent value. The parallel resonant circuit is then connected in series with the 1 kilohm resistor and the combination is connected to the function generator.

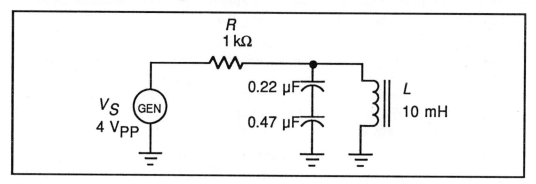

Figure 22–5

19. Calculate the resonant frequency of this circuit. The inductance is known, but you will have to calculate the total circuit capacitance (C_T). Remembering what you learned previously about connecting capacitors in series, first calculate the total circuit capacitance. Record your value. Then calculate the resonant frequency of this circuit and record your value in the space provided.

$$C_T = \text{_____} \mu F$$

$$f_r = \text{_____} Hz$$

20. Using the formula given earlier for the impedance of a parallel resonant circuit, calculate that impedance. Use the coil resistance value that you measured in step 2.

$$Z = \text{_____} ohms$$

21. Apply a sine wave of 3 kHz to the circuit. Adjust the function generator amplitude control for a value of 4 volts peak-to-peak.

22. Monitor the voltage across the 1 kilohm resistor with the oscilloscope. Then, while varying the frequency control knob on the function generator, tune for minimum voltage. Again, do this slowly and in steps. Vary the frequency control slightly and note the new voltage reading after it settles. Continue tuning back and forth until you locate the minimum voltage point. This will indicate the resonant point. At the same time, record the amount of voltage you measure across the 1 kilohm resistor.

$$V_R = \text{_____} volts$$

23. Knowing the value of voltage across a known resistance allows you to calculate the total circuit current using Ohm's law. Do that now and record the current value.

$$I = \text{\underline{\hspace{4cm}}} \text{ mA}$$

24. Next, measure the voltage drop across the parallel resonant circuit. The easiest way to do this is to simply touch the probes across the inductor.

$$V_{LC} = \text{\underline{\hspace{4cm}}} \text{ volts}$$

25. Knowing the voltage across the parallel resonant circuit and the current you computed in a previous step, you are now able to determine the total impedance of the LC network. Do that now and record your value.

$$Z = \text{\underline{\hspace{4cm}}} \text{ ohms}$$

How does this value compare to the value you calculated in step 20?

26. Add the voltage drop across the 1 kilohm resistor to the voltage drop across the parallel resonant circuit. Does the sum approximately equal the source voltage? Explain your answer.

27. Connect your oscilloscope probes across the parallel network by touching them to the two wires of the inductor. Rotate the frequency control knob on the function generator above and below the resonant point and note the effect on the output voltage. Vary the knob slowly from the full counterclockwise to the full clockwise position and back again several times to note the effect that you get. Explain the voltage variation that you observe.

28. Turn off the function generator, but do not disconnect the circuit at this time.

REVIEW QUESTIONS

1. If .22 μF and .47 μF capacitors are connected in parallel across a 10 mH inductor, the resonant frequency will be:

   a. 1158 Hz
   b. 1406 Hz
   c. 1917 Hz
   d. 2323 Hz

2. Series resonance is indicated by:

   a. maximum current
   b. maximum impedance
   c. minimum current
   d. zero current

3. At resonance, a parallel resonant circuit acts like a(n):

    a. low value of resistance
    b. high value of resistance
    c. inductor
    d. capacitor

4. What is the impedance of a parallel resonant circuit with $L = 5$ mH, $C = .001$ mF and $R = 4$ ohms?

    a. 84 kilohms
    b. 125 kilohms
    c. 840 kilohms
    d. 1.25 megohms

5. At resonance in a series LCR circuit, the total impedance is equal to:

    a. X_L or X_C
    b. the coil resistance
    c. $X_L + X_C$
    d. the coil resistance plus any series resistor

EXPERIMENT 23 ➤ Low-Pass and High-Pass Filters

OBJECTIVE

When you complete this experiment, you will be able to calculate the cut-off frequency of low- and high-pass RC filters and demonstrate the effect of frequency changes on the output voltage.

MATERIALS REQUIRED

- Digital multimeter
- Breadboarding socket
- Function generator
- Components
    one–.01 μF disc capacitor
    one–15 kΩ resistor

INTRODUCTION

A filter is a frequency-sensitive circuit whose output amplitude will vary with the frequency of the input. A low-pass filter is one that passes frequencies less than some cutoff frequency (f_{co}), but attenuates those frequency above the cut-off frequency. A high-pass filter is one that passes frequencies above the cutoff, but attenuates the frequencies below the cutoff. Figure 23–1 shows the output response curves of low- and high-pass filters.

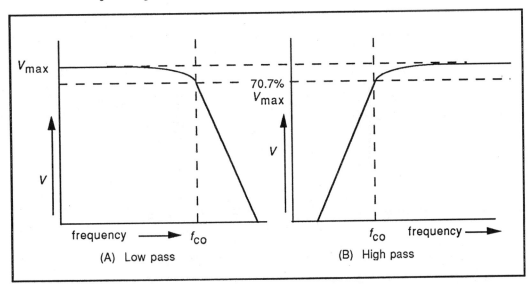

Figure 23–1

Low- and high-pass filters can be made in a variety of ways. The simplest is nothing more than a resistor and capacitor connected as shown in Figure 23–2.

FILTER CHARACTERISTICS

A key characteristic of either a low- or high-pass filter is its *cut-off frequency* (f_{co}). As you can see from Figure 23–1, it is the frequency where the output of the filter drops to 70.7% of its maximum possible output. In a low-pass filter, the output remains relatively constant as the input frequency is increased. As the cut-off frequency is approached, the output begins to decrease. At the cut-off point, the output is down to 70.7% of its maximum possible output. The output continues to "roll off" as the frequency is increased.

In a high-pass filter, the output is at its highest value when the input frequency is well above the cut-off point. Now, if the input frequency is gradually decreased, the output will begin to decrease as the cut-off frequency is reached. At the cut-off point, the output is down to 70.7% of its maximum value. The output will continue to "roll off" as the frequency is further decreased.

In a low-pass filter, frequencies below the cut-off frequency are passed with little or no attenuation; those above the cut-off frequency are rapidly attenuated. In a high-pass filter, frequencies below the cut-off frequency are greatly attenuated while those above the cut-off frequency are passed with minimum opposition. Refer back to Figure 23–1.

The cut-off frequency of a simple RC filter like those shown in Figure 23–2 is computed with the expression:

$$f_{co} = 1/2\,\pi RC$$

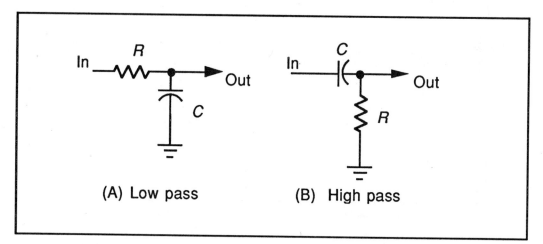

(A) Low pass   (B) High pass

Figure 23–2

Example: if $R = 3.3$ k and $C = .15$ μF, the cut-off is:

$$f_{co} = 1/6.28(3300)(.15 \times 10^{-6})$$
$$f_{co} = 322 \text{ Hz}$$

SUMMARY

In this experiment, you are going to demonstrate the action of both low- and high-pass RC filters. Since you have no means of accurately measuring frequency at this time, only a general indication of the filter operation can be obtained. However, you will clearly demonstrate that these filters do indeed pass some frequencies with minimum attenuation while greatly attenuating others.

PROCEDURE

1. Calculate the cut-off frequency of the low-pass filter shown in Figure 23–3.

$$f_{co} = \underline{\hspace{4cm}} \text{ Hz}$$

2. Assemble the circuit in Figure 23–3 on your breadboarding socket. Connect the RC filter to the function generator output.

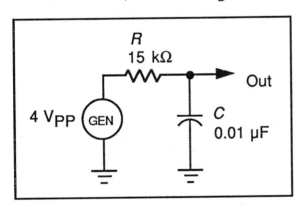

Figure 23–3

3. Set the function generator frequency control to 10 Hz. Then, turn the amplitude control to apply 4 V_{pp} to the circuit.

4. Next, measure the filter output voltage across the capacitor. Record your voltage:

Filter output voltage = \underline{\hspace{4cm}} volts

5. Connect the oscilloscope across the filter output capacitor. While observing the output voltage, turn the frequency control knob to increase the frequency to 1000 Hz. Does the output voltage increase or decrease?

\underline{\hspace{3cm}} Increase   \underline{\hspace{3cm}} Decrease

AC Experiments   **121**

6. Based on the input value in step 3, calculate the value of the output voltage at the cut-off frequency.

Voltage at cut-off = _____ volts

7. Apply a sine wave from the function generator to the circuit at each of the frequencies in the table that follows. Set the circuit input to 4 V_{PP}. As you change the frequency, recheck the input voltage to be sure it remains at 4 V_{PP}. Measure the filter output voltage at each frequency and record your results in the following table.

INPUT FREQUENCY	OUTPUT VOLTAGE
10 Hz	
100 Hz	
200 Hz	
500 Hz	
1000 Hz	
2000 Hz	
5000 Hz	
10 kHz	
20 kHz	

8. Plot your data to form a frequency response curve on semilog paper.

9. Now, wire the high pass-filter shown in Figure 23–4.

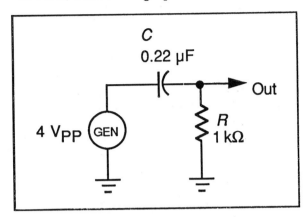

Figure 23–4

10. Determine the cut-off frequency of the high-pass filter in Figure 23–4.

$$f_{co} = \text{_____} \text{ Hz}$$

11. Set the frequency of the function generator to 10 Hz and the voltage to 4 V_{PP}.

12. Observe the output voltage of the filter across the 1 kilohm resistor. While observing the output voltage on the oscilloscope, increase the frequency of the function generator up through 10 kHz. Observe how the output voltage changes as you increase the frequency. State this variance.

13. How does the output voltage vary with an increase in frequency?

_____ Increase   _____ Decrease

14. Apply a sine wave from the function generator to the circuit at each of the frequencies in the table that follows. Set the circuit input voltage to 5 V_{PP}. As you change the frequency, reset the input voltage if necessary so that it remains at 4 V_{PP}. Measure the filter output voltage across the resistor at each frequency and record your results in the table.

15. Now, plot the data in the table to form a frequency response curve on semilog graph paper as you did with the low-pass filter.

INPUT FREQUENCY	OUTPUT VOLTAGE
10 Hz	
100 Hz	
200 Hz	
500 Hz	
1000 Hz	
2000 Hz	
5000 Hz	
10 kHz	
20 kHz	

REVIEW QUESTIONS

1. An RC low-pass filter has an f_{CO} of 23222 Hz. A signal with a frequency of 5.5 kHz will be:

   a. passed
   b. attenuated

2. A high-pass filter has a cut-off of 15 kHz. Which signal will be passed?

   a. 6.7 kHz
   b. 36 kHz

3. The input to a low pass filter is 5 volts. The output voltage at f_{CO} is:

   a. 3.5 volts
   b. 4.5 volts
   c. 5 volts
   d. 7 volts

4. A low-pass filter has values of R = 4.7 k and C = .1 mF. The cut-off is:

   a. 275 Hz
   b. 339 Hz
   c. 469 Hz
   d. 501 Hz

5. The internal circuitry of a multimeter has internal circuitry that causes it to act like a:

   a. low-pass filter
   b. high-pass filter

EXPERIMENT 24 ➤ Band Pass and Band Reject Filters

OBJECTIVE

When you complete this experiment, you will be able to demonstrate the operation of LC band pass and RC band reject filters.

MATERIALS REQUIRED

- Oscilloscope
- Digital multimeter
- Breadboarding socket
- Function generator
- Components
  four–.1 µF capacitors
  one–.47 µF capacitor
  one–10 mH inductor
  one–100 Ω resistor
  four–15 kΩ resistors

INTRODUCTION

A band pass filter is a frequency sensitive circuit that passes a narrow range of frequencies around a center resonant frequency (f_r). All other frequencies above and below the narrow *pass band* are greatly attenuated. A typical response curve is shown in Figure 24–1A.

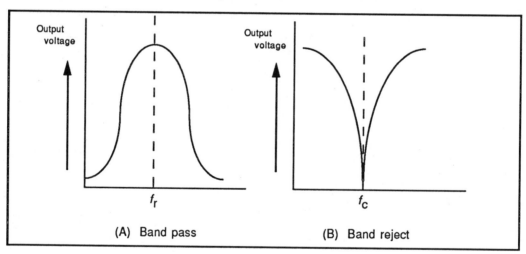

Figure 24–1

A band reject filter is the opposite of a band pass filter. It will reject or eliminate signals whose frequencies fall within a narrow range of the *center* frequency (f_c). All frequencies above and below the center frequency are passed with minimum attenuation, Figure 24–1B. A band reject filter is sometimes called a notch filter because it is used to notch out or eliminate a single frequency interfering signal.

SUMMARY

There are many different ways to construct band pass and band reject filters. LC resonant circuits can be combined in a variety of ways to produce both filters. In this experiment, you will demonstrate an LC band pass filter.

A notch filter can also be constructed with LC circuits. However in this experiment, you will demonstrate the popular and widely used twin-T filter. This is an RC notch filter capable of eliminating a single frequency and those frequencies near it. The center frequency is computed with the formula:

$$f_c = 1/2 \, \pi RC$$

Again, because you have no convenient means of measuring the exact frequencies, you will simply vary the function generator frequency and make note of the filter output response with your multimeter. In this way, you will see how the output voltage changes with frequency in both band pass and band reject filters.

PROCEDURE

1. Refer to Figure 24–2. Construct this band pass filter circuit on your breadboard. The function generator output will be applied to the inductor while the output will be taken from across the 100-ohm resistor. Note that the total circuit capacitance is .47 and .1 mF capacitors in parallel.

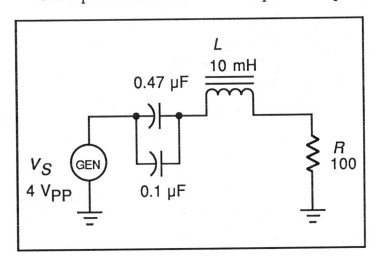

Figure 24–2

2. Using the values shown in Figure 24–2, calculate the total circuit capacitance and the resonant frequency of this circuit.

AC Experiments

$$C_T = \underline{\hspace{3cm}} \ \mu F$$

$$f_r = \underline{\hspace{3cm}} \ Hz$$

3. Set the output amplitude of the function generator to 4 V_{PP}. Then set the frequency to about 500 Hz.

4. Connect the oscilloscope across the 100-ohm output resistor. Increase the frequency of the function generator slowly and observe the output voltage variation. Note the variation. Be sure to change the frequency slowly so that you can get a good indication as to the way the voltage changes as the frequency is increased or decreased. Increase the frequency up to about 5 kHz.

5. Adjust the frequency while observing the filter output. Tune the function generator for a peak output voltage. Note the function generator or measure the period and frequency on the oscilloscope.

$$f = \underline{\hspace{3cm}} \ Hz$$

6. Explain the variation that you observed in steps 4 and 5.

7. Disassemble the band pass filter. In its place, construct the twin-T filter circuit shown in Figure 24–3. Be careful when wiring this circuit, as it is somewhat complex and it is easy to make a wiring error.

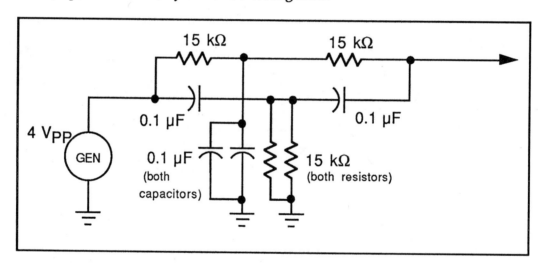

Figure 24–3

There are several important things that you should notice when building this circuit. First, one capacitor value is obtained by connecting two .1 µF capacitors in parallel. Remember that capacitors in parallel add, therefore, creating a .2 µF capacitor.

Another value in this circuit is obtained by connecting two resistors in parallel. Two resistors of the same value in parallel will have a total resistance equal to one-half the value of one of the resistors. In this case, two 15 k resistors connected in parallel to obtain 7.5 kilohms.

8. Using the values shown in Figure 24–3, calculate the notch or center frequency of this filter.

$$f_c = \rule{3cm}{0.4pt} \text{ Hz}$$

9. Set the function generator to a frequency of 10 Hz and a voltage of 4 Vpp. Connect the oscilloscope to the output of the filter. Increase the frequency up to about 1000 and note the output voltage variation. Repeat this several times to be sure you see the effect.

10. Tune the function generator frequency for a null (minimum voltage). Note and measure the frequency.

$$f = \rule{3cm}{0.4pt} \text{ Hz}$$

11. Explain your results in steps 9 and 10.

REVIEW QUESTIONS

1. A notch filter can be made with LC circuits.

   a. True
   b. False

2. In an LC band pass filter, the center frequency is determined by the values of:

   a. applied voltage
   b. L and R
   c. R and C
   d. L and C

3. A band pass filter passes:

   a. one frequency
   b. only high frequencies
   c. a narrow band of frequencies
   d. all frequencies

4. The twin-T is a:

   a. band pass filter
   b. low-pass filter
   c. high-pass filter
   d. notch filter

5. What is the center frequency of a twin-T with R = 10 k and C = .47 μF?
   a. 34 Hz
   b. 47 Hz
   c. 68 Hz
   d. 120 Hz